OUR VISIT TO NIAGARA

BY PAUL GOODMAN

HORIZON PRESS   NEW YORK

OUR VISIT TO NIAGARA

ᕼ 1960

For my daughter Susan

I suppose my stories and novels are, finally, myths—my people turn into nature spirits, genii of the place, or angels. I can't help it, it is how I see (and ineptly behave accordingly). Unfriendly critics have claimed that this makes my fiction "inhuman"; but in my experience, if people are not somehow greater, more portentous, than human, they are not human at all, not even human. I am not sure I have ever met any of these plain folks, though I mix in the city a good deal, just like anybody else. People are either remarkable or batty.

In principle there are two opposite ways of making mythical stories: to start with the American scene and find the mythical emerging from it; or to start with an ancient foreign myth and discover that it is familiar to oneself. (These are, of course, similar to the alternative possibilities for romantic poetry that Wordsworth and Coleridge divided between themselves: to make the commonplace fantastic or to make the fantastic real; not that either stuck to the bargain!)

In collecting my stories of the last ten years, I was astonished at how they fell into these two groups. In the American stories I could not keep Jeremy Owen or the lifeguard or the attendant at Niagara Falls from turning into mythical figures. Yet when I drew from ancient Greece and China, or the Bible, or from Art, I found there my daily business and intimate anxieties—just as I feel that Sophocles, Milton, or Hawthorne are more my personal friends, alas dead, than the literary people I know.

In between these two groups, in this collection, I have put three nostalgic "Community Pieces," to portray those conditions, of community, love, and found identity, under which it is not a problem whether or not Man is greater than man.

—P.G.

CONTENTS

I

AMERICAN STORIES

THE ARCHITECT FROM NEW YORK

1.

The town, he noted, was founded in the 17th century and
grew rapidly till it slowed down; but it continued to grow
slowly and became a substantial center in the valley. Since
1935 it was again growing rapidly. The Berkshires were flaming red and yellow, like a Roman triumph. As the train pulled
in, the architect, without his roll and brief case, felt the excitement he had felt from a child whenever he came to a new
place. To take it in! Now he did it with a practiced eye—
nobody in America knew more about it. There were rarely
any surprises, nothing he had not predicted from a few notes
of history and studying a few statistics. Even so, if he felt well,
as he did sometimes, his wondering excitement might last for
a couple of hours; for there is a difference between knowing

RCHITECT FROM NEW YORK

all about some one and actually meeting her. This evening he felt well and glad to be out of New York. He was Harry Hodges, and here was she.

Low on the horizon the October sun poured through the big trees. There were still big trees even down at the station. Of course in such magical light any place looked lovely, strange. He was pleased that he had a couple of free hours to look and have dinner, alone. He was to meet the building committee at 8:30. Daylight Saving Time, thought Harry, was a good idea because the clear day of dusk was strange. (But when he returned with his roll and his brief case—for they would accept his terms, they always did; and he would take the job, he always did—nothing would be strange, except the art.)

By god, the town had a shape! Harry's breathless relief was like an adolescent's when the blind date turns out to be pretty. A quarter of a mile from the station was a fine green square, bordered by the usual remarkable big maples, with the wooden bandstand well placed off center, the lawn poorly kept. And there was an absurdly small iron fountain, like a prim belle, that—what a contrast to Italy!—had in it all a world of New England shame and sweetness; as if it were sinful to lavish wealth on useless decoration, yet God thought that a pool was proper and there is many such a living eye in Scripture. Harry doubted that any brasses blared from that bandstand any more on Saturday nights in summer; but it was likely still gay and busy on July Fourth and perhaps on the anniversary of Lexington.

It was quite as usual for a New England town like this to have a shape and to have this shape. Why was our friend

16

so moved by it? It was that he had been traveling too much abroad, where *every* town, whether in France or Italy, or Ireland, or even Latin America, had a shape that you could grasp and read off the social history. When you left, you knew that you had been somewhere. But returning home, he would go to our American towns, in the south or middle west—for his churches had won a peculiar reputation as something "special," like Sunday itself, and he was asked to build in all parts; and then he was struck with dismay to see how we have neglected ourselves. The filling stations, the five and ten, the diner, not so much poorly located as with never a thought of location; and the shameful immodesty of the billboards and the neon. He sometimes became so down in the mouth that he could not eat.

He was hungry. He cut across the green toward a high veranda that must once have been "the" hotel, though certainly no longer the biggest and best in a town of this size. And while he walked across that green, in Harry Hodges' breast welled up his plain duty and made him choke, and his ears were aflame. He was bursting with pride. *He*, Harry Hodges, would see to it that the Middle Western towns of America had a shape. If not he, who? (What shape?) He ought to; good, he was *going* to! He had energy, he swung weight, he had the means of the American Institute of Architects. His countrymen would make him a statue in the park. . . . On the left was a statue of James Warren.

Harry's step was light but lagging in meditation, as he cut under the maples across the ragged lawn toward dinner, while the big sun was touching the horizon and flaming in the glass windows.

17

2.

Surprisingly, in the shadows he was confronted by a monumental building on his right, that he had not noticed although it dominated the New England square, as it should, for it was a church. The church had scale. It was small and looked big.

Despite its absurd premise of being "Gothic," the architect could not resist a smile of approval. Maybe it was only the dusk and the magical clear air but, really, that church was very good. Maybe it was that it was surprisingly Gothic of 1875 and quite out of place; and of course it was not out of place at all, and certainly not Gothic at all, but the yearning of an individual Romantic for some richness and color in New England 1875. Who? For a moment Harry racked his brain for the architect's name. He was annoyed, for it was a famous name that he knew perfectly well. He paused and became aware that he was smiling with recognition, and with unembarrassed formality he nodded his head to the other master. And why shouldn't he go in and visit, since he had come?

This was odd to do, in America. When we are in Europe, we walk into every little church, partly because we're there for that, but partly because we know that *in* there, however humble the building, we are likely to be astounded by some imperishable gesture of spirit, an altarpiece, a window, a sepulchral effigy. We come on Moses in San Pietro in Vincoli and say, "For heaven's sake!" In our country, we have not had so many centuries to scatter human treasures around, nor, in the time we have had, have we given our genius lavishly to this kind.

The pointed half-shutters of a side entrance were flung wide, like cardboard angel's wings, and Harry entered.

To his astonishment, the last rays of sunlight flamed into his eyes through a window of Charley Tiffany's, made long ago when that artist was first inventing the glass and was inspired by the angel pre-Raphael. The sheep in the picture were comical and Jacob looked like a divine oaf, and the beads of the border were gurgling and shouting in the light like a one-year-old for joy. The glass window was heavenly innocent as, in that period, was possible *only* in America. Harry was unable even to smile, for his eyes misted over. He blinked them. The sun set and the twilight came rapidly on.

Naturally a roomful of Charley Tiffany's early work, before he became a manufacturer and a patron of the arts, was a rare experience. Even in the rapid gloaming the glass gave off color. Electric lights went on; and as he unhurriedly went up one aisle and down the other, studying the pictures, Harry was like that fellow who lay down just to take a nap but fell asleep; he had come in just to have a look, but he became absorbed in what he saw.

Who? Who? He kept trying to recall the name of the architect. Nixon? Roberts? He knew that it was the master himself and not a disciple, for it had the original definition: the arbitrary Gothic turning at once into a robust Romanesque, full of feeling, and discovering in the solid Romanesque a new Romanesque of masonry that would soon appear, in vast spans, in the secular buildings of Louis Sullivan and Adler. The onset of modern construction. 1875—certainly around 1875—he wouldn't be off by five years; but what the devil *was* the fellow's name? Nixon? Robertson? Hendrickson? Harrison? (He winced at the thought of Harrison.) Nixon was the Vice-President.

Somebody's *son*, that was for sure. Everybody was.

The architect touched the granite with his hand.

Panicky he consulted his watch. 8:30 on the dot! His dutiful unconscious kept good time. He fled from the building, even though he would hardly be late. Outside it was dark. He asked his direction from the first passerby.

He was not going to have any supper, and he realized that he was ravenous.

3.

The rectory, where they held the meeting, was on Duane, off the business street, in a dark-red brick building with gables, in an ambiguous neighborhood. The committee was all assembled in the parlor and was indeed a little anxious, as provincial people are, whether the great man from New York might not show at all. 8:35. But the doorbell jangled, the minister went to welcome him, and the architect came in hatless and breathless. They recognized him from his pictures in *Life,* and everybody stood up for the handshaking.

"That's a *noble* pile there on the square!" he burst out oddly, without waiting to be introduced. "That's why I'm late. I went in to look around and—there it was 8:30!"

"Not late at all, not at all!" protested the minister. "The others just got here."

"I was *surprised* to find a building like that in the town!" cried Harry, gasping.

"I want you to meet Mr. Foster," said the minister, "the chairman of our committee. Mr. and Mrs. Foster."

"The green is nice too; even better if it's kept ragged," said Harry.

"Pleased. Did you come up on the 8:12?" said Foster. He had a rasping voice. "That one is always late. Why didn't you tell him to take the express?"

"But I did recommend the 6:30," protested the minister. "This is Dr. Alexander."

"Pleased, I'm sure," said the architect. "No, I did take the early train, but I got lost—"

"Mr. Tom Hawthorne," said the minister. "He's descended from the novelist's father's brother—I tell you so you won't ask, ha."

"Are you!" said the architect. "Let me tell you right now, if you people are going to put up a modern building here, you'll have to go far to compete with a building like that, put up in the dark ages after the Civil War. I'm not sure I can match it," he said modestly.

"And Mr. and Mrs. Parsons," said the minister.

"I *am* willing to try," said the architect and held out his hand.

He detested these committee meetings that he ought, with his sociable disposition, to have enjoyed; for art is lonely and these folk were collaborators. But the bother was that they were not collaborators, they were not peers; they had no confidence in what they wanted and needed, so they didn't talk up. They wanted to be bowled over by him, and then to

21

leave everything in his hands, including *telling* them what they wanted and needed. They didn't take themselves seriously. But he had found from unhappy experience that if he took them seriously and tried to draw them out, then they walked roughshod over him and intervened in artistic matters in which they had no competence. So instead he dictated and demanded, which he hated. It isolated him. He felt in danger on his eminence.

"Shall we sit down and get started?" said the minister briskly. "Does any one want a liquid refreshment?"

"Imagine!" persisted Harry, as he sat down, "my walking cold into a strange building and seeing twelve windows of Charley Tiffany's! Next time I'll bring a photographer and you'll have them in color in the *Forum*."

He was persisting in these remarks about the church on the green partly because he *was* still there, having left so rudely; but partly also to create the tone for the meeting, cultural *and* informal, giving himself very much the advantage. This procedure was dishonest and he knew it, yet there was no help for it, for it was how he was, familiar with the muse, burning for fame, and needing to get the upper hand so that he could do what he wanted. There was no way to be honest with people. He used words like "noble pile" because they did move him and he really wanted English to be like that; but he knew that they had an odd effect and he capitalized on it.

The doctor had been the only one to listen to a word he said anyway. "What building is it that you're talking about, Mr. Hodges?" he asked sociably.

"Please call me Harry," he said. This was not to be pally,

but because he was embarrassed by being called mister. He looked at the doctor in blank surprise. "Is there another building in this town?" he asked unbelievingly.

"I'm sure I don't know anything about it," retreated the doctor. "Only, you said you were admiring some building—"

There was something in the tone and countenance of the famous guest that made everybody suddenly pay attention.

"I mean the church, of course," said Harry in the silence. "The big gray one on the green."

"*Our* church?" cried Mrs. Foster faintly.

"*Your* church?" said the architect. His face fell. Something was wrong. "I went in on the way here from the station. That why I'm late."

"Not late at all!" cried the minister. "Why do you keep saying you're late? Naturally!" he exclaimed, rubbing his hands, "you dropped in on our old church to see. What could be more natural?"

"But—" said the architect.

"He means the Monster," said Mrs. Foster, who understood what was the matter.

"Oh no, he can't mean the Monster," said Mr. Parsons.

"Yes, he means the Monster," said Dr. Alexander.

"Not the *Monster?!*" almost screamed Mrs. Parsons.

"Well!" said the minister jovially, "he's got to see it sometime! We can't keep our old building hidden from our new architect forever, can we?" This struck him as a jolly idea, of concealing a large church on a public square, like stealing a grand piano, and he gave it a good chuckle. "Ha! ha! So you see, sir," he said, "why we want to get rid of that one and build something new and modern and fitting the worship

of God. That's what *you're* here for. We held a meeting.
We'll get Harry Hodges. Who else? The best, sir. They call
it the Monster."

For a long moment the architect had not a blessed word
to say. He wore a feeble smile. He was at a loss.

"Tell me," he said finally, "do you have your announce-
ment out in front there on the green? I mean the name of
your congregation and pastor and so forth."

The minister reddened. "Of course," he said sharply. The
question did seem to him in poor taste. Joking aside, it *was*
rude to ask if they kept their name hidden. After all, there
was nothing shameful; they had not built the church, it was
a hundred years old. He decided that it was simply a poor
joke. "Prescott Green Congregational Church. D. T. Wieck,
D.D., Pastor," he said proudly. "Sunday October 4, *The
Saving Power of Prayer*. Right out on the lawn and tall as
a man!"

The architect closed his eyes. "I saw that sign," he said.
"If I close my eyes, I can read it off right now. *The Saving
Power of Prayer*. October 11, *Hope*. That's right, isn't it? I
saw it and knew it was your church, and that that was the
church I came up here to replace. But I never did see it and
I walked in. . . . Tell me, who built it?"

"I couldn't give you a clue," said the minister.

"A chap named Richardson," said the doctor, who knew
about such things.

"Yes, Henry Richardson," muttered Harry. "H. H. Richardson—H.H.—" And there, to their amazement and somewhat alarm, except that they didn't know what to expect
from a famous artist from New York, Harry Hodges turned

white and fell back in his chair and almost fainted away, as
the full force of his lapse of memory, of his self-betrayal by
his own unconscious, smote him between the eyes. He even
understood the details. The "Richard" in the name he had
forgotten was King Richard Second deposed by Harry, for he
had seen Shakespeare's play the very evening before. And
H. H. Richard*son* was—Harry Hodges, a murderous son.
This was the simple personal guilt. But underlying these
personal motives, and far more important and personally
terrible than any personal motives, was the social fact that
we in America are forever in a state of ruthless change. Monumental works, built of materials that should last two thousand
years, will be demolished in one generation, and with them
the builder's name. And yes! by a fatality, it is precisely the
loveliest and the best that must be destroyed the soonest and
the most ruthlessly, as if God had a hatred of excellence.
Who can build in stone under these conditions?

Such was the *fact* of the architect from New York as he
cringed in the chair before them, with his mouth open, and
his chin on his breastbone.

"Gentlemen! and ladies," said Harry drily, recovering his
wits. "My considered advice is that you stick with that fine
edifice of Richardson's on the green." Edifice was another of
his words. "Learn to like it. You'll thank me. I'm saving you
money and trouble. Let me tell you—I know—the Tiffany
stained glass alone would warrant preserving the building
even if the building were mediocre. But in fact the whole is
high minor art of the first rank, and I'd be proud to do
as well."

As he said it, Harry already wondered how much of his

enthusiasm did arise from the magical light of sunset and the manic aftermath of deposing papa.

"The stained glass. He's talking about the windows," cried Mrs. Foster faintly.

"The sheep, it's too much!" said Mrs. Parsons and got up hastily and left the room.

4.

There ensued a peculiar debate between Parson Wieck and the architect from New York.

The minister was thrown into confusion by Harry's praising the old-fashioned building, for he had been the moving spirit in inviting him up. What was happening?

Wieck was a large fair-haired man with a good voice, a fair education, and a gift for creating a friendly atmosphere. He was an adequate pastor of the flock, but he was not quite grown-up. The little boy in him was always trying to say the right, the mature, the sophisticated thing that would show how precocious he was. This had gotten him handsomely through the seminary to a wealthy pulpit and prestige in the synod. But since, after all, he didn't understand what he was talking about, whether about psychoanalysis or crisis theology, ever and anon he was left high and dry. The irony was that deep down he did have a puritan abhorrence for the church on the green because it was ornate and catholic—his feeling for a bare functionalism was genuine enough—but this he could no longer remember, and he would have been ashamed to say it.

Harry had not yet made up his mind whether to accept the job or reject it. After all, Henry Richardson was dead and life must go on. Why shouldn't these folk have their way? Yet he found it hard to take their esthetic judgment at face value. What did they *really* have against the building? He asked them. What really did they have against the building? Had they outgrown it? Didn't it function any more? Had the neighborhood degenerated (become Negro)? Why couldn't they sell and find an equivalent site and move? Maybe the town could have *two* interesting churches! With this happy inspiration, Henry Richardson got a new lease on life.

But instead of an answer to his pressing questions, Harry was treated to the pastor's lecture on organic architecture! The trouble with this four-bit lecture on honest form and function, however, was that it had long ago been delivered by Henry Richardson who learned it from Ruskin and others; and Richardson had taught it to Louis Sullivan; and Sullivan had taught it to Frank Lloyd Wright; and Wright had taught it to Harry Hodges. And when he was himself a younger man, Harry had broadcast it far and wide, in his classes at Harvard and in the architectural journals, until it penetrated even the Sunday papers and the radio and finally became the mature and "tough" wisdom of Pastor David Wieck. And now curiously, the moral of this lecture on the American style had gotten to be the necessity of knocking down Henry Richardson's ornamental church, the Monster.

But Harry loved decoration. He didn't think the church was a monster at all. In principle it was as absurd as you pleased, but things were not so simple. There was a man there.

Listening to his own opinions played back to him on a poor tape, Harry was less and less convinced. "How much money do you have in your building fund?" he asked suddenly. "Can you *afford* a new building?"

"$238,420," said Mr. Parsons, who was chairman of Funds for the new Building.

"There you are!" crowed Harry triumphantly. "You don't begin to have enough money for what you want! At present prices I couldn't promise you what you ask for less than a million and a half megabucks, plus my fee." And he spread out his hands graciously, as if that settled the problem to everybody's satisfaction.

"Not so fast, young man," said Mr. Foster, with a voice rasping like iron. They were the first words he had uttered in the discussion. "We have the heaviest endowed congregation in New England, and *we* shall take care of the finances."

As if shot, Harry turned to this new voice and flushed. He recognized the boss. "Cut the shit," he said brutally, dropping his guard in order to throw his punch. "*Why?*" he said menacingly, "why do you mean to tear down that fine building and build elsewhere?" But as soon as he heard that voice, he had known the truth.

Mr. Foster bared his teeth in a yellow smile.

5.

"It's none of your business, young man," said Mr. Foster. "But since you ask me, I'll tell you."

Harry knew him well—he had sat with him on twenty committees—the aged American businessman who has worked hard and skillfully and has retired rich and prestigious. Now at leisure he gives his time to serving the community, in philanthropies and churches and schools. He is well trained for this, he has connections, he knows administration, public relations, fund-raising by horse-trading and covert blackmail; and he can give himself to these enterprises with a ferocity that is not possible any more, without landing in jail, to private persons not working in a good cause. A man like that is free for the first time in his life and he rides high.

"I suppose you've sold the property already," said Harry.

"You are right."

"Well, if you have you have. What's all this palaver about?"

"*We* didn't start any palaver. You mistake yourself. We asked you up here to design us a new set of buildings in Dorchester Heights. Are you interested or not? If you are interested, what are your terms—for a set of preliminary drawings? But you—is it your custom, young man, to teach your clients their own business?"

"Yes, it is," said Harry. "What else did you sell?"

"Really!" exclaimed the chairman. "Really! This is an *odd* way to do business. I'm not sure I see the necessity for it." He was, rather naively, taken aback that the architect had an acumen that among his business colleagues he would have taken for granted.

"Did you, then, sell out the Green?" asked Harry with a melancholy pleasure.

Foster tapped his fountain pen angrily. "*Quite* uncalled

for!" he said. "Quite uncalled for!" He flushed. "Sell out?!
Really, Mr. Hodges! We have had title to Prescott Green
since 1754—*isn't* that long enough? Now we can put the
investment to better use. An enlarged school. A psychiatric
clinic—" He was somewhat honestly indignant, for he did
not weigh the values like the other man. "Explain yourself, sir!
what do you mean, sell out? There are other uses for money
than to tend a field of weeds." His face was purple.

"Please, Humphrey," said Mrs. Foster, taking her husband's
hand.

"Yes, a psychiatric clinic," said Pastor Wieck.

"Shall I get you a glass of water?" said Mrs. Foster. "Doris,
get him a glass of water. Please, Mr. Hodges—"

Harry had finally closed his notebook with a snap and put
it in his pocket. Nevertheless! he could not forbear pursuing, with a melancholy rapture, his vindictive examination,
not otherwise than a jealous husband continues to torment
her, and himself, even after he has found out the truth.
"What is to become of the hotel on the Green, Mr. Foster?"
he asked, closing his eyes to review the scene of the *flagrans
delictus*. "The hotel, Mr. Foster, the library, the statue of
James Warren, that building on the south side with the flag—
is it the Grange?"

"*I* don't know what's to become of the Hotel Prescott, I'm
sure!" cried Mr. Foster. "Is the town never to grow?"

"*Mr.* Hodges! Don't agitate him!" pleaded Mrs. Foster.

"It *is* a handsome parcel of real estate!" continued Harry
inexorably. "You certainly *have* been heavily endowed.
There'll be a new Statler Hotel, a supermarket, a very *grand*

cinema—and—the promoter is P. W. Finch, Incorporated," he said positively.

Now how in the devil did he know that? wondered Foster. It was *absolutely* confidential. It was this fearful doubt, of how far this diabolic man's knowledge extended, and what he was merely guessing at as an expert, that was choking the old man and making it hard for him to breathe, not otherwise than the wife in the situation chokes up and becomes dumb, as the evidence turns up, and who knows what further will turn up?

But Harry was no longer fighting for Henry Richardson. He was fighting for his own immortality, and losing badly in the contest. Just as the statues went down on the Green. Just as the statues went down on the Green. Who cared about James Warren? (Who *was* James Warren?) With a stammer of embarrassment he was fighting for his country, and losing badly. Even so! though he was losing, there was something in him indestructible and he knew it. The art was indestructible. The idea of his country was indestructible. He himself didn't come from these hills but from the Hudson Valley on the other side of the border, near Red Hook, where they have thrown the new Rip Van Winkle Bridge across to Kingston.

"Is the town never to grow?" he repeated the other's remark thickly. "Mr. Foster, what will be the shape of the new town?"

"The shape! the shape!" spluttered Foster, and fell to the ground with a stroke. For it was not with impunity that a businessman in his late sixties meddled in serving his community.

Even while the man was falling down, Harry was quickly

calculating: "They'll now go to Robbins and Peters to do the job. But I'll get to them first and make them see it our way. At least I'll try."

for Percy

OUR VISIT TO NIAGARA

> "Meanwhile, the specious present,
> the intuited duration, stands per-
> manent, like the rainbow on the
> waterfall, with its own quality un-
> changed by the events that stream
> through it."—William James

1. *The Niagara River*

I was bored with the past life from which we had come, I
was not interested in the family visit toward which we were
going; but on the way we drove by Niagara Falls. We came
to the Niagara River outside of Buffalo and turned along it.
I was keyed up and I thought the icy emerald color of the
water peculiar and remarkable. My wife exclaimed with a
forced, yet not unfelt, enthusiasm. She had lived in these
parts when she was a girl. Now she was afraid—she was afraid
of me—that I might not be moved by Niagara Falls, that I
might consider it ordinary or childish or stupid (qualities that
unfortunately she could not distinguish) to be moved by
Niagara Falls. Out of her past, so poor, she thought, in contrast to my past, she was about to offer me Niagara Falls, and

I might regard that offering as not much. But these fears that I guessed in her were groundless, for although I have come to lead among people a spiteful and miserable existence, I still have pure enough in me the ability to be entranced by a geological splendor. I knew, with a quiet confidence and a breathing expectancy, that I should indeed be excited when I came to see Niagara Falls. I looked hungrily at the deep and swift green river as we rolled along. I drove erratically. "Keep your eyes on the road," said Isobel, pleased at my interest. "Over there are all electro-chemical plants on the other side. Look, Ready," she said to our little boy, *"that's Canada!"*

"Where's Canala? I didn't see it—" cried the four-year-old, as if it were a herd of cows or a pair of horses that we had flown by on the road and called his attention to the sight too late, so that he was always desperately looking back.

"All that land on the other side of the river. That's *all* Canada."

"We come to Niager Fa's in five minutes? You said so. You'll show me?" He was afraid that we should also fly by Niagara Falls. "Is they a bridge?"

"The Rainbow Bridge?" repeated my wife still another time. "Lower down there's the Lewiston Bridge—that's the Gorge." Out of her childhood past she kept evoking, in a mesmerized tone, the words "Rainbow Bridge," "Gorge," "Goat Island," "The Whirlpool." I found it pathetic, but not antipathetic; my teeth were not quite set on edge. "Don't worry," she said, "you won't miss Niagara Falls. We'll get out of the car."

Out of the car! The child smirked with anticipation. We

had been on the road two hard days. In order to alleviate his impatience, we had kept anticipating Niagara Falls—"Wait till we get to Niagara Falls! Tomorrow Niagara Falls!" Isobel obsessively repeated to him that from the middle of the Rainbow Bridge one got a good view of the Horseshoe Falls, and I kept trying to safeguard him from disappointment by explaining to him that we wouldn't go across a rainbow, it was just the name of a bridge. "Is they a rainbow?" asked Ready.

First he used to say "Nyaza Fa's." By the time we got to Skaneateles and Cayuga, he was saying "Niara's Fa's." And since Buffalo he had learned to say "Niager *Falls!* Niager *Falls!*"

The city grew thick around us and I paid attention to the wheel. We could hear the far-off booming of the Falls.

2. *Approach to the Falls*

Soon we could see the white mist shining through the trees and smell the ice-green spray; but I took my time looking for a place to park, for I no longer felt *eager* to see Niagara Falls. Yet my face was flushed and my voice had heady tones; but I had lost contact with them. I could not hear the booming any more—the pedal-point had been held too loud and long —but only confused murmuring, some one in the other room talking in his sleep.

If I had been alone, I think, I should have come to terms with my embarrassment as follows: I should have made a little bow to Niagara Falls when I saw him, and spread my lips in a smile, and sketched an informal salute, thus limiting the occasion to a small friendly encounter, as I am used to when I suddenly come on the moon on a country road. But now I was embarrassed for Isobel, to watch me encounter Niagara Falls according to some expectation of hers, as if she were the donor of Niagara Falls, for so she had appropriated it in her girlhood. I could not find a parking space and lost my temper; I cursed because it cost us fifty cents to park the car and we were poor.

"We'll stop only an hour," she said timidly, "just so you can see it. They expect us this afternoon."

But my loyalty rose in me, for I knew that Niagara Falls was important to *her,* and I said brutally, taking the blame on myself, "Oh drat your mother! she won't die this time either. Since we came so far—now that we're here—come, Ready, on to Niagara Falls!"

My wife was burning with impatience; I did not realize that it was despair, that she had already unconsciously given up hope of seeing Niagara Falls, as she sometimes decided at the very beginning of a copulation not to have an orgasm. "We go out on Goat Island," she said. "That's—yes, it's this way. It's this way." She led the way.

The boy was dancing. He was making the tiny bob of his head that he makes when a promise is really to be fulfilled; the chief part of his excitement is that his trust in us has been confirmed.

I could again hear the booming. To my surprise, I noticed that the smell and the rush of waters were coming from the other direction. *Up*stream. How was that?

"Niara's Fa's! Niara's Fa's!" cried Ready, as we came onto the stone bridge.

"No, that's the river *going* to the Falls," said Isobel. "The Falls is there where it's going over. We have to go out on the *island* to see."

But he had run ahead and was already throwing sticks into the boiling river and climbing on the parapet to watch his boats go under. He would whirl the stick with all his hard might and let go; and sometimes the stick flew, and sometimes it dropped at his feet while his own body tried to fly through space.

Isobel impatiently walked ahead and came back. She wanted us to see the *Falls*.

—As for me, I had turned pale. *The broad Niagara River was coming downhill toward us on the bridge.* There was a transporting smell of the oxygenated water. I had not counted on this slope of water. Seeing it, I quite forgot that I was meant to go on to see Niagara Falls. Obviously this, this *flow* of water bore everything before it, but we persisted on the bridge. All of the Great Lakes was coming on. Obviously to me in my poverty it was this *copiousness* of water, visibly accelerating from the horizon and looming to engulf us, that promised something—everything—I was not interested in either achievements or catastrophes. I do not need a spectacular Falls. The good smell was so strong it stank. Recovering from my astonishment, my ears ringing, I began to breathe evenly. Far off, at about eye level, the broad water was always dividing into its two channels.

My wife was annoyed that I was moved before the proper time to be moved. Yet automatically she found herself repeating a lesson of long ago, and she said, "It has all the power of the Great Lakes behind it." To her acute embarrass-

ment she flushed and thrilled at the words, that were so evi-
dently true. "Now that's *enough*, Ready!" she cried irritably,
"let's go and see the Falls."

He jumped down from the parapet obediently; and I too
was content to be led away, for I had had my Niagara Falls,
as in a company of sailors on the town, one fellow is more
calm and rational than the others because he has already had
his party. So habitually, I have my party (I see to that)
very quickly; and then, secure from disappointment, I can be
tolerant and serviceable.

3. *On Goat Island*

As it is, we are protected by our social customs from ever
seeing Niagara Falls except by chance. There are prescribed
vantage-points and boat-rides and guided tours, carefully
fenced to be safe for the multitudes who visit these dangerous Falls. These call attention to this or that aspect of the
Falls, and every such aspect is noteworthy and, in the nature
of the case, uninteresting, domesticated. The environment is
shopworn. No doubt everybody feels the same and would
like to exclaim, as Hawthorne did,

> "Oh that I had never heard of Niagara Falls till I
> beheld it! Blessed were the wanderers of old, who
> heard its deep roar, sounding through the woods, as
> the summons to an unknown wonder, and ap-
> proached its awful brink, in all the freshness of native
> feeling. Had its own mysterious voice been the first
> to warn me of its existence, then, indeed, I might
> have knelt down and worshipped."

And still another century has passed since then, more and more populous.

It had been hard to find a parking space, and on the rock ledge there was a great crowd elbowing to stand at the fence and watch Lake Erie falling into Lake Ontario. There was considerable talk, that sunny afternoon, about Red Hill who had just gotten himself killed going over in a barrel made of inner-tubes and piano-wire. Red had tried for the notoriety, in order to make a living and pay for his beer; yet it was also the case that, like his father, his life had been curiously bound up with the green River. He was a "River man."

The color of that scene is extraordinary. The water is emerald, the foam has a touch of yellow; the mist and the air are shining; and the strata of rocks are a faded maroon streaked with gray-green. The vast amphitheater is glowing. But then—superfluously, or like a bolt of magic (perhaps it comes to the same thing)—shines the rainbow in the mist. One racks one's brains: where before has one seen this unique coloration? And suddenly one remembers: it was in a cheap chromolithograph of Niagara Falls! The violent caricature has betrayed its original to a T.

I stood at the fence. By experiencing it, I could see how a minute alteration of attention, a tiny false note, could change the magic Manitou into the vulgar postcard, not otherwise than those alternating figures-and-grounds of the psychologists flicker and make you sick. The scene did not fail continually to provide a false note. Far below in the basin the ridiculous little steamers, *Maid of the Mist I* and *Maid of the Mist II*, were busily chugging around and around.

"Well, it's the honeymoon's second disappointment, Niagara Falls," said a jocose fellow.

But Ready was smirking and bobbing his head in ecstatic recognition of the rainbow. It was there forever in the mist, it did not fly by. Beside himself with excitement, the boy fetched a stick from the thicket and flung it into the rainbow.

4. *The Cave of the Winds*

Now, however, I had a delicious and redeeming experience that has made me glad forever that I visited Niagara Falls. I say "redeeming" in a pregnant sense, for it was a kind of religious experience.

As a girl, Isobel had never descended to the *Cave of the Winds*. This was a guided trip among the fragmented rocks at the foot of the Falls, behind the sheet of water. We went to the pavilion. The fee was a dollar and a quarter each, and no children allowed. "It's not worth it, let's not—" she said (it used to cost half a dollar and they were too poor; now it cost a little more and we were too poor). I insisted. I parked Ready with an ice cream soda with the matron, and I laid down our sacrifice on the counter.

"Right this way, sir!" exclaimed at once a burly attendant, a kind of Turkish masseur. "Men this way! Women that way! You meet afterwards in front of the elevator." His tone was a command.

He led me to a clammy cell in a cold room. "You strip here. Underwear and socks too. Like your mother made you. I'll bring your duds. Put cash and valuables in this box and give it to me."

"I have no cash or valuables," I said.

"So much the better! No need to apologize."

I stripped. The floor and the stool were wet. I felt uncomfortable and exposed. He came back with a flannel monkey-suit, a pair of crude canvas slippers, and a flaming yellow oilskin and hood. "Put these on and go out to the elevator." The shoes were miserably wet.

When we were gathered at the elevator, men in yellow, women in black, I saw that we were neophytes. We were the fat and the lean, the tall and the short, of the Americans. At once our guide appeared and marshalled us into the cage. He was a large jolly fellow, in a habit that fitted; his manner was unmistakably malicious.

Ready caught sight of us in our strange costumes, he stretched out his arms and uttered a despairing wail; but the door slammed behind us and we descended.

"We are now going down through two hundred feet of solid rock—" began our guide. "Such and such tons of water are falling every second." The walls of the shaft were sweating like the tunnel of the IRT subway at 190th Street in New York City. Our shoes were wet and pinching. The fog, as we emerged, was thick. It was hard to see. There was nothing to see.

"*This way!*" roared our guide above the roar of waters. One could make out a boardwalk and wooden steps winding a short distance among the rocks; but nothing of any interest. He herded us out onto the walk and at once we began to be assailed by the wind and the shower. Nothing could be seen in the fog. We moved cautiously along, single file. "Watch your step! now for it!" roared our guide; and he led us where the buffeting was harder and the flood more blinding and drenching. That was "it." There was nothing to see.

It was evident that we were simply being hazed. The walk went on still a little way, where one could see still less and be still more uncomfortable. And now our shepherd was laughing at us.

According to their characters, some of the sheep began to be angry, some confused, some alarmed. I, identifying with the malice of the inventor of all this, began to be delighted. Once one accepted it *as* nothing; and indeed it was even pleasant to face the furious sallies of cold water (though it was not worth a dollar and a quarter).

We came to the climax and stood on the last platform, drowning and gasping. Momentarily the fog blew away and through the downpour we could make out a rudely lettered sign:

No Zmoking

Almost everybody was willing to laugh a little.

—This trip at Niagara Falls is our Mystery of Eleusis. One offers sacrifice and is taken in tow. One is stripped of his clothes and of the things of this world. One is subjected to the healing elements. And at last one is initiated into the American Hoax. . . . I should not record it here and give away the secret, except that it is precisely when the facts are

known to us through and through that the gullible can feel
most gullible.

"Well, and how did you enjoy your experience?" the Turkish masseur asked me blandly, as I dressed.

"Frankly, I enjoyed it very much. I enjoyed it immensely,"
I said, and gave him a quarter tip.

But some of the others, less established in philosophy,
could be heard to mutter darkly, and they did not tip him at
all.

5. *The Horseshoe Falls*

Returning, I was holding my boy by the hand and we
watched the Horseshoe Falls. Refreshed by my shower in
the waters of Lake Erie, I was no longer perplexed by the
notoriety and venality of Niagara Falls. The coloration of
Niagara Falls did not oscillate into a chromolithograph of
Niagara Falls; but the fact persisted as it was, continuously
coming and becoming: that the ragged water rounding the
deep bend under the cloudy sky was falling into the Gorge
whence rose a strong voice, and mist. For his part, the small
boy had played enough at throwing himself into the water
in sticks and riding the current; he was content to stand still
and watch like a grown person, but smirking none the less
and bobbing his head in excited appreciation.

At a certain moment—I could tell by the tingling in his
hand—his excitement gave way to orgastic wonder. He was
very still, and then he said, "It keeps coming."

The Niagara kept coming; and without even the illusion

of seeming to pause at the brink, the ocean poured over. The weight of water gathered speed and crashed.

6. *The Whirlpool*

Isobel had, quietly, become frantic. Always looking for the Whirlpool. As we rolled northward along the Gorge—she was driving—suddenly she would pull over to the side of the road and jam the brakes. We would get out of the car to look at the Gorge, but this was not, apparently, the place; and we went on. I assumed for a while that there really was a particular place she was looking for, that embodied her Niagara Falls. She referred vaguely to the Whirlpool; but it was not the Whirlpool plainly marked on our map that she was seeking. Also, she cast hardly a glance at the Gorge and rapids as they spread before us different around every turning, washed always with the colors of Niagara. She kept looking away to the other side of the road, where their house had been, if indeed it had been, if this was the road.

She had offered me her Niagara Falls, as a kind of peace offering or an appeasement, since she could not (would not) generously give me what I wanted and what was my due. The bother was that she did not *have* an available Niagara Falls for herself, nor to give. As for me, I am not vindictive; I was quite willing to share her remembered enthusiasm and to admire Niagara Falls. But then, of course, I had to admire what *I* saw in Niagara Falls, and in the manner that I admire something, and this, of course, served only to estrange us further. What I could not (would not) do was to give to

her my Niagara Falls, to share with her my impressions of
Niagara Falls. (I am made anxious telling it with all the safe-
guards of literature.)

I refrained from raillery at her sentimental journey, and
perhaps this was my mistake, for sometimes a burst of anger
brings one sharply to the present actuality, to experience. If I
had rallied her, her eyes would have flashed, her cheeks become hot, and her chin as stupid-stubborn as her mother's;
nor is she unattractive when she looks that way. But as it
was, we kept dutifully piling out of the car. I held the little
boy firmly by the hand so he would not tumble down the
slope, for he was fiercely yawning, hardly able to stand on
his feet.

Nor was there a Whirlpool either, not in the sense of a
maelstrom, a yawning spiral in the swirling waters that one
could go down into if one had the courage (courage she
had), as the Chinese magician descended via the whirlpool
to hell, and danced his dance. What they call the Whirlpool
is where the foaming Niagara makes an acute meander—that
will soon cut the barrier and leave behind an oxbow—and
everywhere there are confused and whirling waters.

I dared not look at her disappointment. Instead I looked at
the mighty scene that did not disappoint, and recurs, shining emerald and maroon, in my spontaneous recollection,
with the bellow of the Falls. All this scene, I could see, was
fresh and recent and in the act of rapidly changing: the
"ancient" Gorge was only a few thousands, a few scores of
thousands, years old; soon it would again look different—the
meander straight, the oxbow left behind; and the overthrust,
the famous escarpment of Niagara, was being eaten away

before one's very eyes, back toward Lake Erie, for the Falls erodes the softer understrata and the roof comes tumbling down. I could not help comparing Niagara against the standard of the Hudson of my own childhood, the valley cloven through pre-Cambrian granite, and the valley itself long ago drowned.

A tiny distant man was fishing on the bank. It was obscure to us how he had gotten down there.

I dared to look at her. I said gently, "Can you remember, Bella, who first told you that the Falls had behind them all the power of the Great Lakes?"

We could speak quietly for a moment, for Ready had fallen asleep at our feet, and so a burden had dropped from our shoulders.

Surprised by my question, she screwed up her face in a frown. She had a headache. She could not remember, neither who it was, nor how old she was, nor in what circumstances it was. But the tears started into her eyes, her frantic face relaxed, and she began to sob. She ran sobbing into the car, bawling.

All the years of her girlhood they had kept her at a strict boarding school, far from Niagara Falls. But she was first afraid, then ashamed, then she would not give them the satisfaction, to bawl for her loneliness. Nor was it any use. She had wanted to play the piano, but her widowed mother could not pay for lessons at the school and she was not allowed to touch the pianos, though there were six and they were idle. She was frequently "insubordinate," and the punishment was to sit up in the cold before dawn. There was a piano in that room and she once defiantly played on it loud through the night.

I carried the sleeping figure of our little boy to the car and laid him on the back seat.

She could not, by trying, give me the loyalty, the identification, that might perhaps have made living with a person like myself worthwhile. What she did for me—it was everything she did—she did as a duty that she had chosen, also for herself, that she had chosen but not that she wanted. Then when from time to time came a crisis and I happened to need affectionate support, she was disloyal and abandoned me to my detractors. Or again, she was sobbing for the fatality that exiled her to living with a person like myself who could only make her lonely and frightened, although there seemed to be other opportunities to live a little happier. (Just as I compel myself to live where I get not what I need, yet not nothing; except that I do not sob for it, but, bravely enough, hammer out my impressions of Niagara Falls.)

Or, simply, the headache in her temples made her whimper, a headache not to be alleviated by weeping, for it was the stretching of wide eyes of fright—near-sighted eyes behind horn-rimmed spectacles that she would not take off.

I took the wheel and we drove onward toward Ontario. Soon the river, as we glimpsed it, had become a gentle lovely river moving toward its sea. Our little boy was sleeping in the back seat. Finally, between two hills, we could see the inland sea. I was describing to my wife—sharing it with her —Lorado Taft's fountain-figure of *The Great Lakes* that stands in front of the Art Institute in Chicago. She has before her five great shells that cascade one into the other: Superior, Michigan, Huron, Erie, and Ontario—and so out to the open sea—all ingeniously placed and characterized to symbolize the actuality.

A LIFEGUARD

1.

Two fat yellow ropes, stretching across the sand into the surf, marked off the area for the exclusive use of the Beach Club, and the members had Tom, their own lifeguard, on his perch. But the other bathers, especially mothers with small children, would set down on the sand pretty close to the Club's ropes, where they could feel secure because Tom was near.

There was a certain amount of class-spiteful humor as to whom, in case of a necessary choice, the lifeguard would plunge in to save first, a member of the Club that paid his wages or a drowning child outside the ropes. Inevitably, each time the talk recurred, somebody pointed out that when the *Titanic* sank, "Women and Children First!" meant women and children of the First Class. Because of a TV program, people in 1958 were astonishingly informed about the sinking of the *Titanic* in 1912. But everybody really assumed that, like anybody else, Tom would do his best to save everybody, whether they paid his wages or not.

He was a good lifeguard but on the conscientious side, considering that people went swimming for fun and fun has a factor of risk. He was studious among lifeguards, a student of Oceanography at New York University, a member of Dr. Neumann's team that measures the waves. Tom could predict the tows and the swells, and tell you how many hundred miles away the storm had raged; and he had a keen intuition for the formation of the sea-pussies, those sudden serpentine eddies, a few yards wide, that pull the strongest swimmer out to sea before they loose him—which is all right if he's a strong swimmer and doesn't panic. Unfortunately, Tom believed the obsessional proposition that an ounce of prevention is worth a pound of cure, and he blew his whistle too much. The members of the Club didn't like to be whistled at; those outside the ropes didn't pay much attention.

Shrill blew Tom's whistle.

The swimmer, a couple of hundred feet out, paid no attention.

"Oh, toin off dat whistle!" said a gentleman of the Club who had been reading *The Hairy Ape*.

The swimmer went his leisurely way, already in the fringe of the dangerous sea-pussy, the outsweeping tow.

Stepping into the surf churning about his knees, the guard blew a terrible blast and shouted, "Hey you! out there! come in out o' there!" He looked a fine human figure, our champion against the dangerous elements, his eyes sparkling with concentration, clothed head and shoulders in purpose, while up around his waist foamed the breakers. Some of the bathers outside the boundary began to shout at the swimmer who was also from outside the boundary. At last he heard them, and for a moment he faltered in his stroke and seemed in a panic, whether because of their shouting or because he felt himself in the grip of the strong sea. But he recovered, fought to a new course, and headed toward the shore.

Satisfied, Tom waded onto the beach and returned to his perch and his cigarette.

The swimmer, however, was not satisfied at all, at all. Up to his knees in the water, he came over to the rope and barked, "Hey you! up there! you whistle at me?" He was a big shaggy fellow, with black tattoos, peevish because of something his mother did to his father long ago; because he had quit high school; because his car burned oil.

"Yes, I whistled at you," said Tom.

The other gripped onto the rope in his passion. "What in hell is your business, you whistle at me?"

This Tom did not judge worth a reply.

"You whistle at me I punch you in the nose! Why in hell you don't whistle over on that side o' the rope where they pay you?"

Tom came down to the water's edge. He darted back like a sandpiper in order not to get his toes wet. He said courteously, "I whistled at you because you were too far out in a sea-pussy."

"Sea-pussy!' " cried the shaggy one. "Sea-pussy!" He appealed to one and all with a roar of rage, "*Sea-pussy!* you hear him?"

"Yes! you couldn't see it, but I could see it," said Tom, unconsciously quoting a sentence out of the ancient times, and it tolled in every heart like a bell.

It touched exactly the wrong note, of ignorance. "Listen to him! he whistles at me! I been swimming in this ocean before you was born, you—you college-boy."

Tom turned his back on him and walked away. By this time there was a small crowd of spectators.

"That fellow does look, Tom, like he could take care of himself," said one of the ladies of the Club, kindly.

Sudden anger seethed in the lifeguard's heart. Why was he wasting his summer? They were not even loyal! Whirling, he came down to the shaggy swimmer at the dividing rope, frowning brow to brow. But when he burst out bitterly, his words were directed at them one and all. "If I *minded* my business, if I let somebody drown over there, *then* there'd be a hullabaloo, wouldn't there? *Never* hear the end of it. You make me sick." His speech came in gasps. They were now both in a passion.

"Yah! yah!" said the shaggy one.

"You shut up," said Tom. "So long as *I'm* in charge here, I'll give the orders. Any questions? F'Chrissake, how *else* could I do?"—he ended with a weak and piteous appeal.

Pitiful, for of course he was *not* in charge. He had no major premise. Nobody had given him any mandate whatever.

"Naturally if somebody was in trouble, you'd jump in— we know *that*," said a woman.

"When I patrol the shore, you won't even *begin* to get

in trouble!" said the guard arrogantly and bitterly. He meant it and he was proud of it, and he hated the carefulness that he was proud of.

"Maybe *that's* the trouble, Tom," said a gentleman of the Club, who was a physician. "The trouble with you, Tom, is that you forestall every emergency. But nobody will co-operate with anything before he's convinced that there *is* an emergency. You come through in an emergency and you're a hero, everybody's crazy for you. You act like a prudent man and prevent the emergency from arising,, and everybody's sour on you because you're a worry-wart. Yes! and you're sour on yourself." The physician said this with extraordinary melancholy, his voice drowning in its own undertones, so that people couldn't help looking at him in wonder. He was a physician.

But there was another elderly man, from the other side of the rope, not a member of the Club, and he was a famous Constitutional lawyer. "No, I beg to differ," he said in his rich voice. "People *have* to protect themselves from interference; how can they let themselves be pushed around? Consider the present difference of opinion. If the members of your Club there don't like the way the young man fulfills his responsibility, let them turn him out! let them vote him out and fire him. But what recourse do *we* have, here on our side? *We* neither hire nor fire. Are we to submit without question? But the answer is obvious: we can go and set a hundred yards down the beach, out of the young man's surveillance. Nothing hinders. Now why don't you do that, madam? Yes, you, madam." He turned the question point-blank at a Mrs. Roche.

She blushed. "Why—you know—it's safer for the children, of course."

"Precisely!" said the lawyer, having scored his point. "What you people don't see *is* that you put *him* in an intolerable position. What warrant has he? He has no warrant, and nevertheless he has an obligation. Now really! let's face it! If you people want to avail yourself of Tom's services—and the facts speak for themselves—why else camp just here on all this magnificent beach? If you want him to be your agent, then you ought, however informally, to make a compact and constitute him as your seashore chieftain. I for one say, Hurrah for Tom! Three cheers for Tom!"

Swept by moderate enthusiasm—and also delighted by the play of ideas, which were not a dime a dozen at the seaside resort—nearly everybody sang out, "Hurrah! hurrah! hurrah!" And especially the mothers of small bathers frantically clapped their hands.

This proposal and the acclamation were intended, of course, to mollify the angry lifeguard (as, for instance, they would have mollified me and made me blush and, like a fool, take on another duty without pay, except for a uselessly expensive piece of luggage tendered at the end of the season). On Tom they had the opposite effect. In the first place he thought he detected a note of mockery in what was really good-humored pomposity. The reasonable language of the jurist was a little over his head, and he was stung to fury. But more important, and no mistake, the proposal *was* a trap. For what would he get out of it? He had accepted this summer job in the sanguine hope that there would be pretty girls available at the Club—no objection if they also had money. But it hadn't worked out that way. There were no pretty girls at the Club. If a pretty girl visited, she passed him by. The matrons and the men who courted his attention didn't interest him. But meantime it seemed to him that, always a hundred yards away, up the beach, down the beach, anywhere but where he was chained to his post, there was a bevy of pretty girls, or a solitary girl who had surely smiled at him as she strolled past and out of reach.

The jurist had accurately sized up the social situation and proposed a practical remedy. But it was the physician who had vaguely and feelingly glimpsed the live, underlying causes that were not so easy to remedy. Namely, that Tom was hedged in by his duties, and that he hedged *himself* in, more than was necessary.

It was at this laden moment that Colonel Burke, the manager of the Club, came down to the shore to see what the fight was about and what the crowd and the cheering were about. From the outset his attitude was unsympathetic because he didn't like to see that crowd on both sides of the yellow boundary; he didn't like it at all. It was strictly not exclusive. "What goes on here?" he said in a peremptory tone.

"Oh I whistled some guy in," said Tom.

"He whistle at me!" said the shaggy man.

"I told *you* to shut up," said Tom.

"*You tell me shut up!?*" shouted the man.

"Shut up," said the Colonel. "What, was he drowning?"

"No, he wasn't drowning," said Tom drily. "No, he wasn't drowning yet. There he is, ask him." His voice rose. "How in hell would I know whether he was going to drown? Use your head."

"He's not one of our people."

"No, he's not. What about it?"

"What's the matter with you, Tom, anyway? We're paying you a good salary. What in hell business is it of yours if this person—"

"That does it!" said Tom, and cut him off; almost as if to prevent him from saying something dreadful. "I quit!" he shouted. "You can take your lousy job and shove it!" With a snort he yanked the whistle with its elastic over his head, and childishly he slammed it down on the sand. He jostled his way through the crowd and jumped over the rope and kept going. Then awkwardly he had to return back across the rope and walk to his perch for his cigarettes and lighter. He was acutely conscious of how ludicrous this all was. He stalked off the second time with great dignity.

There it was. Now neither those in the enclosure nor those beyond had any lifeguard at all.

2.

By a couple of miles up the beach, the young man had gotten over his first mad and was breathing more calmly. All around there spread, sublimely, nothing; the sea, the sun, the fertile Void, from which spring the monsters of the deep. It was five o'clock.

"*Hurrah for Tom!*" Their shout rang in his soul. "*I quit!*" His shout rang in his soul.

After awhile both shouts faded and left him in silence, in the hiss and moan of the breakers.

He was out to the lonely dunes, for nobody walked out this far. Sometimes one of those odd hiking couples, man and wife, sixty years old, bent under their knapsacks, the man in shorts with knobby knees and she looking very sensible. But today there were not even the sandpipers.

The sun was small and red. Up near the dune was a magnificent writhing driftwood, a satiny gray stump and its roots, undermined long ago in Nova Scotia and carried here by ocean currents that Tom could have named. He stood and admired it and stroked it. On an impulse he picked up a great black sheet of wet seaweed with a lettuce-curl and tails, and he flung it wide around his shoulders like a cape. New clothes! He had *shed* his old purpose and duties; he took on, not another purpose, but loyalty. *To* the elements. He was no longer our humane guardian against them.

Calm, joy, and violence were his immediate rewards. He stripped off his human mask.

Or we could describe his state another way and say: that the very soul that is conscientious when the environment is other people, is *large* when the environment is only sea and sky.

However it was, as he sported there, it seemed to him absurd to be wearing swimming trunks and he stripped them off too; and he hung them on a branch like a tan weathered flag:

"MAN WAS HERE. 1959."

For the first time all summer, he himself ran down with a shout and dove through the breaker. The water stank with algae. Shaking the hair out of his eyes, he headed into the sun's spangles. West! West! He *played* with the sea-pussy. He whispered to her that her name was Evelyn. For a quarter of a mile he rode, as in triumph, the golden trail. Meditatively he headed back toward shore, swimming an old-fashioned Australian crawl. All in all, he had a good swim in the choppy water, and he came out of it much the happier.

Shrill blew the whistle, and the shore-jeep ploughing up the sand whined to a stop.

"*Hey you!* Come out o'there! What in hell do you think you're doin'?"

It was the constable on his round.

"Are you whistling at me?" said Tom innocently, but he could not imagine who else was there to be whistled at.

"The matter?! Nude! that's what's the matter. Indecent exposure! What d'ye think this is, nudists?"

"Indecent exposure?" said Tom, wondering, and looking down at himself, surprised. "Indecent exposure to whom?"— But instead of protesting, he burst out laughing, loud and long, like the Olympians, a laughter that was not letting off tension, nor was it resignation; but Tom's laugh was round and solid laughter at the absurdity of mortal beings. Fetching his trunks, he went docilely along back to the club to get his wallet, and then to pay his $25 fine at the county seat.

BATHERS AT WESTOVER POND

1.

There were two men in the moonlight, arguing in low tones. The jealous husband was lying in wait. His elderly friend was trying to get him to go into the house.

Suddenly, both fists, the angry man pounded on the barn door. Inside, animals stirred. "I can't help it," he said choking, "it has me by the throat."

"Maybe you have *it* by the throat," suggested his friend, the doctor.

"O have a heart, Manny! don't give me moral lectures when I'm in trouble."

Carefully watching and biding his time, the way you handle the wilful drunk, the insanely jealous, the doctor said nothing. Through the trees shone the moon, on the buildings, the mailboxes, the road around the bend. "Well, Mark Armisted?" the doctor said finally.

"Don't *call* my name!" the farmer gasped, stricken. "*How* can I appear? Yes, I have *it* by the throat. I spend *hours*, do you hear me?, thinking up *schemes*, to *prevent* her from being happy. I!" As if it could not happen to him. "But when I eat it, it sticks." He began to cough. "See? she was supposed to be back by ten." It was ten fifteen. "Maybe there isn't even anything between them, how do I know? She never *told* me." He had never asked her. He was again assailed with remorse. He coughed. The image that always came to him was Desdemona; he had seen the opera. "I understand," he said, "that we can no longer live according to the usual ideas— there are no usual ideas. . . ."

"Ideas! It's you who have ideas. Why don't you simply face it? that you are suffering and you *don't* understand it, and that makes it all the worse."

"All the worse!" echoed the farmer and the tears finally welled into his eyes. What he wanted was, after all, sympathy; not out of self-pity but to assure him that he was not isolated in his evil frame of mind. The scene blurred for him.

"I'm sorry you're in trouble, Mark," said his friend, seizing the advantage. Perhaps now was the moment to get him to go in. "Come, let's go in," he said gently, firmly.

But just at this moment they heard them coming up the road. It was twenty past ten. Giddy laughing, leisurely approaching. It was the leisureliness that was the coup.

They had been singing, *On the Town, Fancy Free*, and by now they were mockingly down to the bare rimes, "Spree," "you and me," and "wheeeee." Whee-he-he-heeeeee. Wendy sprinkled the tones through the night with her beautiful coloratura, and Mark hated his wife bitterly because she sang beautifully.

They appeared around the turn. To his surprise—both relief and disappointment—they were three, not two. He had been lying in wait for two. But with Wendy and Perry there was another sailor. Mark sprang at them from the shadows, his face ugly in the moonlight, and her giddy high-E became a cry of fright. He seized her by the shoulders and threw her to the side. "Get into the house," he said hoarsely. He had no voice. His rage was no longer spontaneous.

But she stayed there a long moment by the road, waiting—it seemed—for Perry to protect her. Instead, the sailor drew back a step, and rapidly she crossed the field and disappeared in the house. The door slammed.

Mournfully Mark turned on Perry. (By now they both looked pathetic figures.) He took the two slow steps across the road and deliberately struck him, aiming the blow, but not in fury to destroy him but as a man deliberately picks a fight; he slapped him hard across the face. "Hey there, what goes on there?" said the buddy, and closed in and threw a punch that Mark blocked. But the doctor intervened with the authority that stops a thing short. He brushed Armisted away with his shoulder and said curtly, "Go in," and he said to the other sailor, "Keep out of it." Armisted lost his animus, his chest fell in depression, he looked hopelessly at his hands, the tears started again into his eyes, and he reeled slowly across the field and disappeared in the house. The door closed more dully. Perry did nothing at all and the mark shone on his face in the moonlight.

"Why did you let him get away with *that?*" demanded his friend indignantly.

"I have no rights," said Perry surprisingly.

"But you said you were in love with her."

"Yes. Yes, but I don't mean to come across. You *know* what I mean, God damn you. God damn that cold fairy!" His anger flowed back in him and the color spread all over his face. "I should've knocked his teeth down his throat." Perry lived in the conviction that Wendy's husband was sexless and that that was why she came out. Vaguely, somewhere, he knew that this was not the case.

He said, "Let's go," and walked brusquely away. His buddy caught up. They went back down the road and disappeared around the turn.

A few moments later, to the doctor's astonishment, they were again singing, their voices fading in the distance. He shrugged.

The door of the house opened its bright rectangle and Armisted came out with a pail and crossed over to the chicken house.

2. *Dr. Grove's Poem*

As he walked back through the old locust-planted town, the doctor saw that the tree trunks were rough and massive, their foliage black and delicate against the sky, the houses wan in the moonlight: so he projected his own personality. His thoughts had turned away from the disturbing scene he had witnessed, but he was disturbed by the ring of his heels on the pavement, as if a man had no right to exist and go.

A couple passed him by, the man talking earnestly in a low voice, the woman weeping. They passed, and the doctor halted and looked back after them. Then, as he walked the few streets more to his home with its shingle, Dr. Groves made the poem:

> When the couple passed me on the walk
>   and the woman was crying out her eyes,
> the man continued in earnest talk.
>   His tone was measured, his manner wise,
>
> there was no doubt that he was right,
>   but something was wrong, something was wrong,
> as they drifted past me in the night,
>   as I hurried along, hurried along.

3.

Wendy was blank, having sung the little child asleep.

She had been singing the *Coventry Carol* and the *Raggle-Taggle Gypsies*, such songs as express good-bye and separation. It was not that she was thinking of these things—she was not thinking of anything—but they were the songs that came to her to sing. Often she felt blank and did not know what she was feeling, but her behavior revealed it to others. Armisted was sensitive precisely to these signs, more than was useful, for he addressed himself not to what she *was* feeling, *where* she was, but to what she might be feeling if she felt it. She did not understand that what she did but did not feel nevertheless had an effect on other people. And he, by knowing what she was feeling when she did not, uncannily threatened her; she was afraid of him, afraid of her unknown self. She was afraid.

Hearing the songs she chose—but the child fell sweetly asleep—he was clenched with alarm that she was going to go away. What he did not notice and make much of was the overt fact that his young wife was singing to her child falling happily asleep.

"What are you thinking of?" he said; but he *knew* what she was thinking of, that was just the trouble. (Often he did, sometimes he didn't.)

"Nothing," she said. "I am not thinking of anything."

"Yes, you are thinking of something—" he said. He could tell that she was thinking of leaving.

"No, I'm not." She was not lying; she was not thinking of anything. She looked up at him with eyes brimful of reproach and fear. Demanded of, she agonizingly felt her mind, and it was blank. "Don't wake up the baby."

"Yes, don't wake up the baby," he said. This was real and they went into the other room.

"You sit there looking defeated," he said. "Why should you feel defeated?"

"Defeated? How am I defeated?" There had never been a battle.

"What's the matter now?" he cried. "Why are you looking at me reproachfully?"

"Nothing's the matter, dear. I don't feel reproach. Really I don't." She could hardly be heard.

"*That's just it!*" he almost shouted. "You won't give me the satisfaction. You spite me by talking in a low voice. You won't give me *anything*—neither demand nor reproach. I *know* that your mind is blank, you aren't thinking of anything. But *why* aren't you?—" He wanted to say, in his jealous fit, that she was thinking of Perry, and to have her say, yes, she was thinking of Perry, in order that he could cling to this and torture himself with it. But it was too humiliating for him to begin. "I don't believe you," he said.

She hung her head as if she had been struck a dull blow on the nape of the neck, and her eyes became wet. "Why do you bother with me if I am so worthless?" she asked. "If I don't give you anything at all and if you think that I am a liar. That's what I don't understand, why you keep at me if I make you so unhappy. Why you don't tell me to leave."

"Ah! that's what you want! At last! at last!" he cried, beside himself. "*I* am to take the responsibility. So you can go to Perry. But I won't give *you* the satisfaction!"

"That's a lie!" she cried, with flashing eyes. He had found the key to make her angry: she was "unjustly accused."

"You sit there thinking of Perry to rescue you," he tormented her, "defeated by me and thinking of him. Why don't you admit it?"

"No, I was not." She looked at him with disdain. But he did not feel humiliated; rather, pleased and more self-confident because she looked so bright and real when she was flushed and angry. He smiled.

"What are you laughing at?" she asked, stung.

"Yes. Yes. I was thinking of your question: why do I bother you, what do I see in you? I know the answer. Because you are brave. It's your bravery I love and it's your bravery I can't bear."

She was bewildered. "How am I brave?" She was beguiled because she knew that it was a great compliment but she did not understand him. She looked up, as she often did, like a small pupil in a classroom.

"You are brave because you won't give in. You are unhappy, unhappy here with me, but you stick out your jaw and clamp your teeth like grim death, you go blank and don't know what you're feeling at all—you will do anything and go to any lengths, but you won't be compelled. You want to be free! What's wrong with that?"

He said it with pleasure and with his better self that was not jealous. But she took it badly, to mean that he was giving her her freedom. What would she do with freedom? She became panicky. She felt he did not want her any more and this desperately wounded her vanity.

Controlling her panic, and to control her panic, she said in a flat voice, "Yes, I am going to go away and leave here. Yes I am, I am, yes I am. You always put me in the wrong, day after day. Every day is the same." Everything she said was music, and this too turned into a grevious chant, "Yes I am, yes I am. You trap me, I don't trust you."

"No, you're not!" he said, and stood barring the door with his arms, as if he could stand there forever and keep her a prisoner. He was clenched, as when he first heard her singing the songs, but worse. For now she had said it. But his heart was bounding and hammering. For both of them the child in the other room did not seem to exist, although one could still, if he listened inwardly, hear the faint tones of singing.

4.

The courage, the kind of courage, that Mark ascribed to Wendy did perhaps belong to her; but certainly it was an image of his own character. He willed it, and would not resign. He willed to live satisfactorily, to make his life succeed as a whole, even though the conditions of our lives do not seem to permit an organic success. He risked chaos, he did not stop making his demand. His troubles with his wife were of a piece with the rest of his existence; he saw this and tried to generalize about himself; and he became confused by principles, which are nothing but thwarted deeds. He thought, and often spoke, like a social-psychologist; he suffered torment like a possessive peasant; he was sexually open like a child; he aspired to justification like his Calvinist ancestors. He clung to farming as a way of life, although in our society it was not a way of life because there was no wilderness; it gave plenty of small anxieties but no big challenge and no big satisfaction. He was successful at farming and that made it all the worse. He knew too much to live the way he did. He implacably willed his marriage to be reasonable and worthwhile, but it wasn't. He was ashamed.

His shame was not that he was miserable, for this he could have borne philosophically. But he was tormented by an idea in which he unfortunately believed, namely that unless a man is primarily happy he cannot realize his powers, and that therefore Mark Armisted was going to die wasted. This abstract thought awakened in him an awful guilt, and he redoubled his strenuous efforts to be simply at ease.

He had the manliness of the old time, by which a man suffers sleepless nights and headaches because of a contradiction between two propositions. And this behavior was *not* obsessional with him, because if he happened to find his way out, or life provided it, he smiled sweetly and slept.

Wendy watched him wrestling this way, when he did not know that she was looking. He used to pace up and down, up and down, and drum loudly on the tabletop with his fingers. Then he would suddenly go out of the house. At these times she loved him and felt for him. But by timidity she neglected to make the simple advances to him that would materially have alleviated his dilemma by a new piece of evidence, a proof that "my only world does not hate me." And because his wife did not help him in this simple way, *she* was his dilemma and he glowered at her with hatred. Feeling this hatred she shrank and could not make simple physical advances. It was when he saw this that he suddenly went out of the house.

He was right to be afraid that she was going to leave him, for harshness can, in the end, drive anybody away. But he was mistaken to fear that she would choose another man against him.

5.

When she came to the interview with Perry, Wendy was carrying a tooled leather purse that Mark had made for her.

The sailor did not notice it. He felt just fine; he had already, waiting for her, had three drinks. He was glad to see

her, he did not notice that she was on edge. She became
annoyed at his roseate cheer and pointedly she called his attention to the bag, for he had, a month ago, enthusiastically
offered to make her one, among a number of other warm
promises. "Mark," she said, "made it."

At that time she had carelessly let slip Perry's promise
to make her such a bag, not realizing how hungrily Mark
listened to every word, to be invited to compete, to be included. And the very next day, more mischievously than
maliciously, Mark gave her the leather bag, "Here is the bag
you wanted." He was proud of it because it was beautiful and
as if commissioned. She was moved. "You see," said Mark, "if
you only ask me for a thing. How else can I know what you
want? Don't you see, Wendy?" In this way he put her in
the wrong and she went blank. "I didn't ask you," she said,
and poisoned his pleasure.

With Perry, however, she was able spitefully to attack, and
so she felt free and emptily happy. "You talked a lot," she
said, "and didn't make the tooled leather bag. Mark said
nothing and made it."

"I meant to do it when I said it," said the sailor cheerfully.
He was immune to this kind of spite. He had a wonderful
confidence that he had what all women desired—if they
didn't, so much the worse for them!—and this harmless
vanity made him so generous and outgoing that it was hard
not to love him, unless you had to rely on him. He had the
beautiful vanity that aims to please, and he did please. But
the woman across from him was in despair, and he was slow
to perceive it.

He picked up the bag and examined the workmanship with

unfeigned admiration. "That's fine work. That's really fine. It's better than I could have made you."

"Thank you," she said drily.

"No, seriously. Look at the ends—" He turned the leather inside out to show her.

She was stifled. Here it was again. The two men were conspiring and she was worthless and had nothing to say. She did not know whether or not it was good workmanship. (*This* was why she could not make Mark feel that she appreciated the gift.) At the same moment she felt a powerful pang of lust and stealthily caressed the serge of the sailor's blouse with her fingertips. "Mark does everything well that he turns his hand to," she said stiffly, to conceal her emotion. "It's too bad that you—and he—that you can't talk to him like a younger brother. Maybe *he* could help you to find out what you want to do with yourself." To give herself a presence, she assumed the role of go-between.

The sailor drained his drink, leaned back, and ordered another. He said, "Mark seems to have all kinds of talents— except what a woman needs."

"*What do you mean by that?*" Wendy became rigid and went white. It was the first time that Perry had made a direct remark, or any remark, about her husband. Immediately she felt dirty and disloyal. She was in a frantic mood and her feelings, suffocation, lust, chill, degradation, succeeded one another pell-mell, and all were climactic.

He laughed, his laugh a little ugly.

With the precise clarity of an insane moment she saw him; that he considered her husband as a defeated rival, and that it was this that gave him his charm and address, which he would not dare against a looming father, sexually powerful. He assumed, he quickly assumed, he always assumed, that he was the victor—but there was never going to be any battle. She looked at him: he was a child. She looked at his childish uniform and felt sorry for him. In a flash she made sense of what had truly puzzled her, their submissiveness to their stupid officers. "I understand you only too well," she said with brutal contempt; "but if you imagine that Mark is not a healthy animal, you are very much mistaken. He doesn't satisfy me because I won't let myself be satisfied; but he satisfies himself, be sure of that. I'd be afraid to deny him. Also—I wouldn't want to." She was flushing deep red, the pulse pounding her temples. She had never before spoken this way to any one, nor used such words.

Perry was stung. "What in hell is it your business what I imagine!" he snapped. "*You* seem to imagine that it's all up to *you*, whether you will or whether you won't. What conceit you women have!" He hated women. He had sat up and suddenly he looked at her with horror, rallying to the defense of the other man's insulted manliness as well as his own. He was outraged by what she had said.

Everybody was against her. Her eyes began to roll wildly.

The young man's native courtesy made him hold back. And now that he noticed her, he began to be alarmed. With a wrench he rose above his hurt feelings and his indignation. "Look, Wendy—" he said; almost he said, "Look, mother—" For he held her in awe, she was the only sensible and mature woman he had ever intimately known and he did love her. She was in trouble. He took her hand. It was lifeless. "Do you know why I love you?"

"No, why?" she said listlessly. She didn't care.

"I love you because sometimes I was able to make you laugh, and you didn't seem ever to laugh and sing." Her face was frozen and her fingers twitching between his hands. "Darling," he pursued gently, "now why don't you and Mark —you and Mark—why don't you and Mark try—"

"That's enough!" she cut him short and stood up. "Put up or shut up. Will you or won't you go with me to Boston?"

Bewildered, he shook his head slowly from side to side, at a loss what to say, but of course saying it well enough by his dumb gesture.

She burst out laughing in her gay and thrilling artist's voice that both gathered force and became lighter as it soared, coloratura, with rolls and trills and scattering a random shower, but true at last to the leading tone and the tonic, and she said, "I shall have at last a place of my own, and come and go as I please. And take the opportunities I choose! To whom am I beholden? and what if I won't? No! no! not at all. But I shall go to Boston, where there is no difference between night and day."

And she flashed him a childlike smile and picked up her bag and left.

6. *Westover Pond*

There was a large pond where the country-folk went to bathe. The water was clear, the bottom was sandy, and the minnows came up to your white toes. There were deep black holes where the bass hid. A mighty willow leaned over the surface and was mirrored in the surface. The afternoon was still. Stiff-legged skippers walked on the tense water. In the silence, a trout leaped and fell like a bell.

In one angle stood the tiger lilies in August. That part was muddy and pond lilies snaked up from the bottom and opened. A frog dove from a lily pad, like a sob.

It was a large ordinary pond lovely beyond anything imaginable. The facing shore was a stony hillside pasture, down to the water; your eyes followed it up to the blue sky, and to a tremendous towering cloud, whose reflection you could see silent in the water, so most of the water looked white. All these things were so strange as to be unbearable. How do we people manage to live on among them?

Wendy came finally wandering by here, carrying her shoes, but the hem of her skirt was soaking wet. With her came clamor, because she was singing, imitating bird calls and the birds answering her sounded off, rousing one another, until the din was terrible and deafening like morning, that tramples on our awaking and rushes by. But pretty soon she went past, walking barefoot on the path, around the bay where the sedge was, out of earshot, and the birds shut up.

7. Bathers

About six o'clock the dirty farmers and tired women and three adolescents came down to wash and swim. They were raucous in a more vulgar and bearable way, calling out *our* calls. Without a pause as they came, the two boys kicked off their brogans and dropped their jeans and plunged headlong with a splash, hitting out for the center, two shining furrows shouting, "Ouch!" "Cold!" "It's fine!" All the frogs dove down to the bottom. The girl made no effort to undress or go in; it was obvious that she was menstruating. She sat down on a rock and lit a cigarette.

The farmers and women disrobed and bathed more solemnly. An elderly man went into the water up to his knees, in the reddening sun. The sun had suddenly dropped another foot toward the horizon and there was a chill.

The boys climbed out, shaking themselves like dogs on everybody. An angry man said, "For Chrissake!" The boys dove back in. "Don't think I'll go in after all," said a matron complacently, half undressed. "Really?" said her friend, "how can you do that way? If I once come down I feel I just have a moral duty to go in and get wet. Brrr. I go zip in, zip out." "That kind of consideration doesn't bother me a-tall!" said the other. "It's a remarkable way to live! it's a remarkable way to live!" said her friend in sincere admiration. The men were uncorking a gallon of wine grown by Italians in California; there was no local wine. Every little while a man or woman walked to the edge and dove or slipped in. The women tended to stand and soap themselves and then swim. Two of the men were strong swimmers and stroked away toward the far shore. The elderly man, without getting wet much beyond his knees, emerged and lit his pipe. He was Dr. Groves. Another man climbed out shivering and set to work making a fire (he was the angry man).

The sun tinged rosy the linen lying in untidy heaps. The orange adolescent boys, but none of the others, seemed to be bashful of their nakedness and tied rosy towels around their waists. Pouting in a mirror, the girl put on lipstick. From the long branch of the willow where I had climbed, over-hanging the water, I watched with envy the rapid swimmers at the far shore, wishing that I were as strong and daring as they. Between the open clouds in the west was a moloch hearth of embers. Our fire began to crackle.

The gallon jug was going around, and most of the folks had put on clean clothes that they had brought.

"We should've brought supper, we could've had it right here."

"Next time."

"No I couldn't, because of the kids."

All at once Mark Armisted was in the midst of them, carry-ing his little girl and bawling in a hoarse voice, "I separated the mother from the child." Because of his loud voice the child began to cry. From where I watched in the tree, he looked again like a man of the old days making open con-fession on the street corner. They crowded around him.

The complacent woman tried to take the crying baby from him. But Mark clutched onto the baby, and must have hurt her, for she screamed. Mark seemed to believe that Wendy had run away to Boston.

Yet the scene was peaceful, as if becalmed. It was the few minutes of the onset of evening when the sun, touching the horizon, has ceased to cast long shadows. The space is like a painter's north light, but red and shining. It is homo-geneous, breathing, quiet. The frantic man; his excited, sym-pathetic, and alarmed audience; and even the scream of the child did not importantly disturb the peaceful ending of day. The birds sang in small bursts as they do at that time.

"She ran away," one fellow said to his friend, "with that sailor who come up from New London. He's in the submarines."

"Maybe she did. But he always seemed a decent sort to me."

From near the sedge came a sickening cry, from the throats of the adolescents who had gone off there to stone frogs. The strong swimmers, on their way back, cut sharply in that direction. Immediately—the time it took me to get out of the tree—the two men and the two boys broke through the brush carrying toward us the clothed and drowned body of Wendy. They laid her down by the fire at the feet of the doctor, and one of the men, snatching up his trousers on the run and awkwardly cramming his feet into his shoes, went through the woods to get his car. Mark Armisted stepped back from our circle with the pained look of a man who has made an important wrong inference and, as if a forfeit, he gave over to the woman the baby who had suddenly fallen asleep.

Groves had rolled the body over onto a woolen shirt. He used me to work her ribs and one of the kids to raise her elbows. He (his metabolism) was a little too fast on the count, and I kept slowing the pace. There was no doubt he meant to pull her through. "Not so bad," he said, "she jumped in there not more than fifteen minutes ago." "What? after we got here?" "*Because* we were here," he said, "—and *two*—and—one—and—two."

I had plenty of time to observe our doctor as I mechanically swung. His face was defiant, as if to say, "This one isn't going to die either." Mark hung over us, with an expression of simple concern. Pretty soon there was a fluttering and she began to breathe and take over on her own.

"Oh good!" said Mrs. Erlanger. Groves stopped us.

The people cheered, or did not so much cheer as finally expel their held breaths in a loud noise. But the menstruating girl burst into hysterical sobbing. Groves sat Wendy up, and she looked about with wondering eyes, then closed them wearily. "Whiskey," said the doctor. It was to hand. "Will you shut that girl up!" he snapped ferociously toward the hysterical adolescent. The fire was roaring hot. Mark said not a word, but smiled a very pure and unmixed smile, almost a grin.

Wendy downed a mouthful and coughed. She seemed tired and she lay down again flat on her back and looked up at the sky.

Then—to our universal astonishment—lying flat on her back, she broke into song and sang the spacious *Clouds* of Ned Rorem, which the composer has marked "in a pale half-voice; infinitely slow, pale," and so she sang it:

> So effortlessly are we not given
> to move on earth as these in heaven
>   clouds, nor without desire
>   to tend whither the airs conspire.

> The clouds exaggerate and pile
> into heights of mile on mile.
>   In the breathing of the universe
>   they drift asunder and disperse.

There was the roar of the car and the fellow came back out of the woods.

"No! she's alive!"

"She's alive. Groves pulled her out."

"No! no! she's alive!"

This curious motto, "No!—she's alive!" seemed to take everybody's rescue-drunken fancy and people kept shouting it rowdily, as a way of exploding their suppressed excitement and joy, and perhaps to deafen the unearthly echo of the song.

"No! No! No!"

"She's alive all right!"

"Couldn't she swim?"

"Couldn't she *swim!* Wendy Armisted?! Are you out of your mind?"

"Stubborn."

"No! no! she's alive!"

8.

Suddenly it was very dusky. The firelight shone on our faces.

The doctor was in a roaring anger, the outcome of his defiance. He did not work it up, as we say, but rather gradually opened the valve and let it roar, it was there always. "Oh, get out of my way!" he pushed a fellow, who would ordinarily have retaliated, but not now.

"What you so mad about, Doc?"

"What am I so mad about? All my life! these idiots! Do

you think I enjoy it? Now see ye to it! see ye to it!" He seized
the questioner by the shirt-front and pushed him again. Out
of the way? *On* his way? "Yes she's alive!" he fairly shouted,
"and what lesson shall *we* learn from this text?"

We formed a decent circle around him, to let him rant.
Almost one expected him to begin by crossing himself in the
name of the Father and of the Son and of the Holy Ghost,
except that he was an atheist. "I'll read you the lesson. She's
alive there because there wasn't a sufficient reason for her to
die, it wasn't worth it. That's it. That's it. It takes a stronger
justification to die—more shame than that! or failure of duty!
or such happiness lost that it's not worth living on again.
Where do you have it? Where do you *see* it in this county?"
He looked around at us with a terrible accusation. Into the
eyes of each one. "Is your marriage so sacred? is your adul-
tery so interesting? which of your writers can motivate a story
strongly enough to end it with a death?"

He turned away in disgust.

"What do you mean it isn't worth it for Wendy to die?"
asked a man offended. "What a thing to say!"

"I mean just what I say. It's not interesting. It doesn't
interest *me*."

"Oh, and are you the judge?"

"Who else?" he said recklessly.

He was speaking recklessly, not what he meant, yet it was
not obscure to some of us what he meant: he meant to say
that *he*, Dr. Emanuel Groves, found justification in keeping
the other people alive, but he did not himself find a reason
either to die *or* to live.

If you have a reason to live—answering the question,

79

"What is the meaning of life?"—then you might have a reason to die, for example to defend your reason to live. And oh! if you are in that happy condition that you do not even need a reason, then you are in fact *making* a reason in your life, you are growing into something, and that fact will be obvious to every awestruck observer, and felt by you as faith. Are you in fact that happy?

As gradually as it flared, the doctor's anger speedily abated. He became habitually compassionate, his shoulders drooping to their habitual depression, and he said gently to Mark, "That's a sick woman you have there. Do you know?"

"Yes, I know," said Mark.

"*Do* you know?" The doctor looked at him searchingly.

"Yes. Underneath I know it all the time, no matter how I seem to act up. I stop, for instance, when her eyes begin to roll. This is what I live with. Also—" he hesitated. The doctor waited. "I do *not* know. How to cope with it. My only world. Do you follow me? If I *knew* what was good for her, I would do it and gladly."

"I believe you," said the doctor.

9.

Mark went and sat beside Wendy at the fire. She was awake and she sat up.

"How are you feeling?" he said.

"All right. I'm sleepy. Can we go home?—Will they let me go home?"

"Yes. Of course. Albie will drive us. Let's go." Neither offered to get up.

It was clear that the husband and wife were not going to refer to the incident any further.

"Where is the baby?"

"Asleep." He got up and brought the baby and she took it in her arms and touched the face lightly, with her finger-tips.

Mark held back a moment, but then put his arm around Wendy. He waited, hoping against hope, that she would lean her head on his breast and perhaps weep. But she did not, no more than she ever had. But he was horribly tired and rested his own head on her shoulder, saying to himself, "I must not cry, it would probably be a bad note"; nevertheless, he at once began to shake with silent sobs. She petted him gently.

In respectful memory of Hawthorne.

JEREMY OWEN

Says Thoreau in a letter: "The
blacksmiths met together looking
grim and voted to have a thunder-
bolt, if they could only get some-
one to launch it; but all the while
there was not one man among
them who could make anything
better than a horse-shoe nail."

But this has not been my experience. I can make a fine occasional
poem if they give me an Occasion.

1.

"Hey, Jeremy, when do we eat?" hinted O'Donell loudly.
He was the Chevrolet agent and he had recently gotten
Jeremy an honest buy, so he felt at home in his little res-
taurant.

But Jeremy was looking blankly at the meat on the grill
that he had mechanically turned off. He did not start, as if
his thoughts had been elsewhere. They were nowhere. He
made the sandwich and brought the dish. Astoundingly he
did not bring the coffee.

The auto salesman *was* astounded. He looked up with
sudden eyes, like a small boy who knows that something is
wrong if the routine is interrupted. But he was not a sharp
observer and he imagined that Jeremy was preoccupied; he

did not see that he was ceasing to be occupied at all. Perhaps he did see it, but could not accept the terrible fact that "Mama isn't going to feed me any more." Their eyes met. O'Donell was abashed to ask for his coffee. But he had to have coffee. "Hey, Jeremy, do you still make that good coffee?" he called pleasantly.

Jeremy was a candid observer and caught the lie. Making an effort of good will, he brought him his coffee. Without apology.

"You in love, Jer'my?" said O'Donell pleasantly. But the perplexity on his forehead said, "Is something wrong, Jeremy?"

Jeremy responded to his forehead and not to his words. His impulse was simply to take off his apron and walk out; but instead he dutifully spelled it out and said, "I don't seem to want to serve you any more, do I? . . . I don't mean *you*, Red Hugh—" As soon as he had said the words, he realized that he had indeed withdrawn from these people and was in a crisis. The sweat stood out on his face.

The remark had a finality that the salesman could only disregard. He sank his teeth in the meat that was, as always, the best, seasoned with a thumb of dry mustard, blackened bits of garlic, and a dab of creamy butter; and he took a sip of the coffee that was the best in that county.

2.

Jeremy Owen's was a jewel of a short-order restaurant; by a freak of luck the small town happened to possess it—and what a difference it made! Jeremy's sign said Good Food without quotation marks, like a fact not an opinion.

After trying other jobs, the young man had hit on this way to make a living. He had no special talents, no particular interests (not in food either), but he had a good appetite himself, good senses, intelligence, and a beautiful serviceable soul; he fed them as he fed himself, taking the trouble. Truck drivers and commercial travelers arranged the schedule to eat at Jeremy Owen's, and he made plenty of money. But he had no interest in making money. He wouldn't feed a man if he didn't like him, but this rarely happened, for people tended to be at their best at his little tables. Jeremy had no conceit about this either. He saw that he had simply gravitated, as if by a deliberate choice, to an elementary role in life that could not fail if he performed at all. He was Mother Nature. He grinned when he first thought of the analogy. (He had a wide grin that flashed when something was neat, even if it was grim.)

Jeremy Owen didn't look like Mother Nature. He was five foot ten and rather spare, with the plain good looks of his frank and serviceable character, with blue eyes and chestnut hair not neatly kempt, and with something unusual from time to time in his expression that might be borderline-insane.

3.

Now they had trooped out, after the lunch hour, the last hot apple pie à la mode. He went to the doorway and looked after them with stupefaction.

Across Main Street, Alex was on a ladder changing the sign

on the movie theater. Lola was window-shopping the silver
dress. Red Hugh was disappearing into Auto Sales. The 2:10
bus pulled in front of the drug store and the basketball team
mounted with their satchels. It was 2:14. On all this Jeremy
looked, and realized that he was not *serious*. Those fellows
working in their businesses were ambitious to make money;
they were married men. Lola was set on making a marriage
in a few months, and she would succeed because she wanted
to. The basketball team wanted to win. To him money and
marriage meant nothing, and there was no game that he
wanted to win.

According to some ideal view, Jeremy *was* serious, for he
was giving a service that they needed and he was doing it out-
standingly. Nevertheless, that view was false, for he was not
interested in these people, to serve them. They did not interest *him*. Just because he was not conceited about his abili-
ties, nor ashamed of his worthlessness, he was able to pose to
himself the naked awful fact: that the people of his town,
who were some of them fine people against whom he bore no
grudge, for he was successful and had no cause of resentment
—those people were of no interest to him, and therefore he
could hardly continue to serve them.

But he did not know any other town, he was in a crisis. As
yet, however, he felt only stupefaction, as if it were they, and
not his own nature, that amazed him. He did not yet panic.

Alex, on his ladder, had spelled out the name. Jeremy did
not take it in as a word, though it was the very movie they
had all been heatedly discussing at lunch. Instead—there
swept over him a wave of nausea, as if he had been eating bad
food, force-feeding himself. When it passed, and the pure

taste returned to his mouth, he had a flashing insight: he had
been existing among these people by making allowances.
Their entertainment was *not* entertainment for him. Their
movie stars were not teasing images for him, and the stories
had nothing to do with *his* problems. Why pretend any
longer? But he had been making allowances for them, for
their business and their entertainment, in order to have his
town at all, a people and place. If he did not share these
fantasies, what fantasies could he share? (In fact, he had not
gone to the movie in a year; he was already hopelessly out of
touch.)

He did not like to be contemptuous—it made no sense—
for what was the use of a small triumph when he was the big
loser? But—just look at that unlovely street! It did not flatter
your eyes! the unproportioned buildings, dingily colored and
without unity of form or material; the bleak road through,
where the immodest cars drove too fast; the lousy chain
grocer—like ten thousand other uninteresting places. Jeremy
realized, with naive surprise, that his own little place was
attractive to him simply because he had made it so. It did
not yet occur to him to become angry and determined to
change the street. Instead, he became uneasy with romantic
longing, and sank into gloom.

4.

He closed for the afternoon and went fishing.

He was afraid that there was "something wrong with him,"
meaning that he was going crazy. But he had a test of his

sanity. If Dyer's Pond and the pretty woods around it would also seem mean and unattractive to him—especially at the end of September—then certainly he was far gone.

Jeremy did not know many poems but he had by heart one that had been printed in the county paper:

Dyer's Pond

You're a sweet limpid pond
to trudge a mile around
   or swim across you idly
   that mile divided by π.

The hatchets of boy scouts
ring out like rifle shots
   through the scrubby pines
   where yellow sun shines,

and through the water where we stand
we see white pebbles on the sand
   and green pickerel about our feet
   nosing if this be likely meat.

(By his measurement, the swim across the pond was only 300 yards and not 560, a "mile divided by π," but Jeremy saw that the poet was right to put it so neatly, and this was for him a great literary discovery.)

The insanity-test was negative. The pond was as attractive as ever. The cottonwoods were yellow, the pines dark. It was hot Indian summer and he soon kicked off his clothes and took a swim. He felt better. He was not estranged from the *world*, for he could always go to Dyer's Pond! Today he particularly scrutinized the purple flowers, the dying weeds, the single-minded ants. It was all of a piece—with his own body—practical, like Paradise. But he was lonely.

Alas! when the human beings appeared in their station-wagon on the other shore—a couple of families and assorted youngsters—there was a tumultuous hiding in the thickets to change into bathing-suits, with piercing jokes. This offended Jeremy; life again had him by the throat, stupefied, estranged. He clenched his fists and determined to swim across and lecture them on their behavior, naked as he was.

For a moment he bethought himself. *"They* seem to be sociable and happy; it's I who am lonely and in dismay. Who asks me? Why should I give them a hard time when they couldn't care less?" Yet he swam in their direction anyway, and when he was about sixty yards offshore he shouted: "For Chrissake! why in hell you need bathing-suits to swim in a pond like this?"

"Can't hear you! I can't hear you!" shouted one of the men. "What you say?" He waded out in the water toward him. "You say can we lend you a bathing-suit? . . . Hey, do we have an extra bathing-suit?"

"Why don't you swim bare-ass?!" shouted Jeremy in a fury.

"Oh. Why don't you mind your own business, Owen?"

His report of the conversation set off a renewed volley of laughter, and Jeremy was stung, and swam away.

It was not that the others embarrassed him or interfered with him in any way. That might have been better, it would have made him fight. He sunned himself on the beach quite as if they weren't there. But how did it come about, he wondered, that he, with the same background as his townsmen, was unlike them in many ways? He did not doubt himself. He *knew* that their mores made no sense. He concluded baffled: he simply did not know enough to answer the question, why people behaved as they did when they knew better.

As he was returning into town, however, happening suddenly on a knot of people, he was possessed as by a demon by an evil thought that human beings were like roaches huddled in their dirty spots, that scurry when you flash a light. This had never happened in his restaurant.

5.

For a few days the passion of Jeremy Owen had a most curious effect on his menus. Since he was not interested in the diners, he tried to interest himself in the cooking. He began to offer fancy dishes studiously copied from Escoffier, and spent hours at night concocting the white stock for the sauces. It was an empty gesture, because he was not an artist.

Amazed, his clients obediently ate what he put before them. But the small town, so lucky in its jewel of a short-order diner, hardly needed or appreciated a learned French cuisine, nor was it very good. Even Jeremy had to laugh at his efforts.

6.

He described the incident at the pond to Julia.

"The man was right," she said. "How *is* it your business if they want to wear bathing-suits?"

"Can't you see? They don't take it seriously or they'd be indignant at *me* being naked."

"Of course they don't take it seriously. It's not a big deal any more. Everybody knows *that*."

"They know it, but they *still* have to wear the bathing-suits!"

"It's for the children," she explained. . . . "Why, what's the matter, Jerry?"

He had fallen silent. Finally, "It's not interesting," he said thickly, "when they behave like that."

The words fell between them dully. What he was seeing was generation after generation, down, down, down. He quietly began to panic.

"What did you hope for?" her voice rose. "Did you want them to lynch you for shocking them, when you don't shock them? Would that be—interesting?"

"Why are you shouting at me?" he said.

"You don't have much sense of humor," she said and laughed.

Her laughter was swallowed in the silence. He was looking at her. She became anxious and touched his forearm. The touch made her amorous, but him cold. They were upstairs at his place.

"Look, Jerry," she said, "everybody knows I spend two, three nights a week here. Does anybody say anything—at the Company—or make me any trouble? It's not a big deal any more. How do they stand in your way?"

She knew that something terrible was happening. He was looking at her, so to speak, objectively. In fact his mind was racing, not helter-skelter but leaping from one vanquished position to another, as a mechanized army leaps ahead with lightning prongs and swallows up all France. *They* were not interesting, *she* was not interesting, *this* was not interesting. He had often asked himself why he did not marry her, or even when he was going to marry her. She played her cards skillfully; one of the thing he admired in her was her skill, even though he was the prey. He was lustful and forward, he had tried a good sampling of the women, but he always found that it was with Julia that it worked out best. Nevertheless he avoided committing himself, and now he knew (he felt he knew) that it was by a deep instinct of self-preservation. With her too he had been making allowances. Can you marry some one, making allowances?

He was ashamed. He felt that he had been lying to her. Not because he had sometimes acted as though he loved her or might get to love her, for that is an honorable experiment; but because he was really making allowances for her.

He rallied to his gentlemanly honor and took her hand, just as if he were responding to her touch. She at once rebounded. "What was that you called out?" she said happily. "Bare-ass! *I* like to swim bare-ass!" And she put his hand under her shirt.

Now he felt his panic. His eyes were glaring and the sweat appeared on his brow. For he felt no animal desire. He did not begin to. Without love, the promise of love—the essence of love is its on-going promise—there is no lust. He took her body in his arms but it was not interesting. He was not used to this absence of feeling, and he could not help but interpret it as a terrible maiming. He thought that this was what he was panicky about. By iron self-control he willed his body to respond. But while they were making love, he kept thinking,

"No one is to blame! no one is to blame! I am not made for this world. It is as if they sent me to the wrong planet."

She, of course, knew that he was slipping away from her and she was invaded by a chaos of sentiments, fear and woe, recrimination and self-recrimination; included in which, however, was also a motherly concern for the man she loved.

7.

Now on October 4 (1957) the men launched and sent into orbit our first man-made satellite, sharing in heavenly motion, freely falling around the world once an hour. In space.

When Jeremy heard about it in his country town, he was mad with joy and pride. As an American, he was disappointed that Russians had made the first successful launching, but this feeling was overwhelmed by his love (and indeed relief) for mankind, who had again done something magnificent, worthy of enthusiasm without making allowances. Something interesting! The names that kept repeating on his tongue, when he read them in the newspapers, were Copernicus and Kepler, Galileo and Newton. These astronomers were for him romance, and there was nobody in that county, or perhaps in that state, who was so proud and happy as Jeremy Owen.

The exploit also frightened him: to think of the hundreds of men on the far-off steppe, and our own soldiers and sailors on the shore in Florida, single-mindedly active like those ants at the pond. To do it! to do it! swept up in obedient activity! So he alternately chilled and was afire with pleasure. He saw the rocket rushing aloft, and finally achieving its swift un-hurried ellipse. It was hourly signalling to us in our language.

Pounding on the latest edition, he sought out Red Hugh in his salesroom. "Well! how's about it?" he crowed. "And what do you think o' that?! It says here—"

But the Irishman's reaction to the new moon was an odd one. Jeremy found it touching. Faced with a real novelty, the cautious Donegal superstitions of Red Hugh's childhood rose to the surface. "I dunno," he said dubiously, "I don't like us goin' in there where we're not invited. My way o' thinkin', people shouldn't step out o' their place. When I was a boy, we knew our place."

Jeremy roared with joy and began to beat him on the head and shoulders with the newspaper. "It's *our* place, Irishman, it's *our* place! Do you think we picked the lock and walked in? Kepler and Newton! Do you think we're whirling up there without trying for it, wishing for it and working at it, till we figured out all the laws of motion? Copernicus and Galileo! Why, they *opened* the door for us and said, 'Boy, welcome home!'"

When he cried out this, that entering into space was like coming home, Jeremy blushed scarlet; and Red Hugh flustered by his enthusiasm and being pounded by the newspaper, blushed too.

All day at the restaurant, however, Jeremy had the melancholy opportunity to listen to the responses of the average man to this wonder of Man. Unable to let the subject drop, he greeted each newcomer with the glad tidings; and he kept tuning the radio to the small moon's hourly beep, for it was a busy moon that came by often. Alas! some persons didn't care about Fellow Traveler at all; others felt nothing but chagrin that the Russians had beat us to it and won a victory of propaganda; and others knowingly pointed out that the satellite proved that our enemies had an Intercontinental Ballistic Missile with a Nuclear Warhead—the polysyllables rolled off the tongue.

"But *men* did it," said Jeremy pathetically, and he repeated the magic names Copernicus and Galileo, Kepler and Isaac Newton.

"Yeah, and the crazy Jew Einstein."

Jeremy looked at him with stupefaction. Yet he was not disheartened; they could not take away his moon.

It was not till late in the afternoon that he got a normal response. A youth came in for a hamburger after the basketball practice. "Say, Jer'my," he said, "what you think about this satellite?"

"God bless you!" said Jeremy. "Yes!"

"You bet, Yes!"

"Isn't it great?"

"That sure is great, because it says here in ten years we're gonna have a man up in a rocket on the way to the planet Mars."

"That's right," said Jeremy, "that's what they say."

"I'm gonna be that man," said the youth seriously.

"I believe you are," said Jeremy seriously, and the tears of pride began to stream down his cheeks as he looked at the youth of lofty aspiration.

"Gee, Jer'my," said the youth frankly and without embarrassment, "I feel like bustin into tears about that satellite too, but I wouldn't dast to cry in public and all. Gee, Jer'my." He looked at the man as if he were as wonderful as the satellite, and suddenly, fearfully, he bolted out the door.

Fifteen minutes later he came back calmly for his hamburger, but the place was closed and on the door was the sign:

CLOSED

Jeremy Owen won't
serve food in this town
until further notice.

8.

He was bent on leaving the town. He was not yet sure that he wanted to leave Julia. He called her up and they sat in a corner in the tavern. He persisted in talking about the Fellow Traveler.

Ordinarily Julia would easily have shared his enthusiasm, the way a loving woman shares in such things, by complacently admiring the exploits and enthusiasms of her baby: he with his eyes on the machinery, she with her eyes on his face. But now just her love was hurt and threatened. She was anxious, finally frantic. It was she who was the child and needed attention and reassurance, which he did not have to give. She hated the artificial satellite. She was jealous of it.

He became mournful. He did not mind her spiteful remarks, which were simply stupid and unlike her; but she was clinging to him when he was bent on freedom. He felt that he was going to do something brutal.

She sat like a block of resentment, intent on her own hurt

feelings, and unable to look at him and say the simple sentence that would have made sense, "Let's *us* go to Outer Space! there's nothing here." Ordinarily this would have been an easy sentence to say, for the town was indifferent to her, it was only Jeremy that mattered.

Instead of doing a brutal act, he tried to sneak away from her by feeling remorseful, and he said, "I'm sorry, Julie—I see I made you fall in love with me. That was wrong. Wrong. A woman like you—a woman like you deserves to have a steady man who can take care of her, but I'm going crazy and I can't even take care of myself. Naturally you want to get married—. Who in hell do I think I am!" he exclaimed. "If *I* don't care for what other people care for, is that *their* fault? Jeremy Owen doesn't go for Lana Turner! Big! deal! Is it Red Hugh O'Donell's duty in life to be interesting to Jeremy Owen? It's not *my* fault either!" he shouted.

"What on earth have I got to do with Lana Turner and Red Hugh O'Donell?" she said, offended.

"Oh yes! oh yes! it's all the same."

"What's all the same? I think you *are* going crazy."

With a shaking hand he lit a cigarette, puffed on it, enveloped his head and shoulders in a cloud of smoke.

"I closed up the diner," he said, "and I'm going to New York."

"Take me with you!"

"No."

The tip of his cigarette was glowing in the heart of the swirl of smoke. As the smoke wafted toward the door on the draft, his eyes appeared, hard. He could see his eyes mirrored in the drop of tear hanging on her cheek. The small word he had said was hanging in the room between their heads. "No."

9.

That night the sky was mercifully veiled in cloud, so that Jeremy did not have to look for the little moon, which he could not have seen anyway. Instead, he himself walked in interminable circles, in and out of town. To an onlooker— but there was no onlooker—it would have been problematic whether or not he would last in possession of his sanity till dawn, having quit his job, rejected his woman, and no longer making allowances.

His mood swung from enthusiasm to stupefaction, from glad surprise that it was so to unbelief that it could be as it was. Perhaps, having suddenly decided no longer to be in- terested when he was not interested, Jeremy Owen was like Adam awaking, to whom everything was a surprise. But who can endure that?

Jeremy was not a church-goer; yet in this crisis of his exist- ence when, arbitrarily, he was going to New York on the first train in the morning, he reverted to an archaic pattern of his childhood and fell on his knees to pray to God. Along- side the bed. He grinned at himself, though wryly, because it was neat. But his behavior was more peculiarly appropriate than he was aware of, it reverted to his ancestors in Con- necticut, religious reformers; the borderline-insane strain was an ancient one. They too, out of the blue, used to make a public gesture and bear witness according to their consciences.

He had come back to his lonely dwelling to catch a little sleep. On an impulse he lit a candle to see by, for that romantically seemed to him to be a warm and "real" light. He felt that his day's joy was holy and that he was "wrestling" and making a "clean decision." And then he was kneeling and the candlelight shone from the table on his New England profile and unruly hair.

The content of his prayer was astoundingly American. "Creator Spirit," he prayed, "do not make me, with my new feelings, stand out as too different from the rest of the people. Granted that I am most often right in my judgments, and they are wrong, let me either be persuasive to others or come to respect them anyway as also having views worthy of men. Otherwise I cannot be democratic. But I cannot live unless I believe that all men are equal. O God Creator of the world! do have made your world so that we are essentially equal and can give and take and come to an agreement. Amen.

"You know I'm not afraid," he said further to God, "to stand out alone for what I think. How could I do otherwise, in your spirit? I am strong and stubborn enough to suffer isolation, envy or disdain, or even the prejudices and penalties of the people. But all this makes sense only if finally I and my people do not fundamentally differ. (May it be in my time! but as is your will.) O God! what is the use of your truth if I lose by it my people? Certainly you can't mean anything like that!"

It was good old-fashioned wrestling with God, that often came to recriminations and taking Him to task.

"Good," said Jeremy and climbed into bed, "that'll work."

He was confident because his prayer was sincere. It cast the burden off his own shoulders, no matter where or on whom or even into the deep blue sea. And sure enough, he at once got his answer, in the form of a salutary admonition: "Jeremy Owen!" something said to him, "you'd do much better for yourself, young man, if you'd stop being the mother of the multitude. You are *not* Mother Nature. Really, the sky won't fall down, nor anybody starve, if you take a vacation, even if you *never* came back." And with this ironical reflection, he fell happily asleep.

10.

It was on the 10th of October that I met Jeremy at the Museum of Modern Art on 53rd Street, looking, or trying to look, at the great *Water Lilies* of Monet on the third floor, the same picture as was destroyed in a fire a few months later. I could see that the young man was highly excited by the picture—as well he might be—he kept changing his position to get it into focus.

He turned to me impulsively. "How you get to *see* that picture?" he asked.

I pointed out to him, sourly, that it wasn't his fault, the picture itself was poorly hung. Typical Modern Museum slovenliness with all their slickness. It was too big for the room it was in, it needed a back-up to see the impression. I showed him where, from the adjoining room, one could get a kind of good glimpse, at an angle, through the doorway.

"I guess that's what we always get," he said wryly, and riveted my attention, "a glimpse, at an angle, through the doorway, if the other people get out of the way. . . . Are there more pictures like that?"

I assumed that he meant *Water Lilies* by Monet and I assured him that there were many, including the remarkable ones, even bigger than this, at the Orangerie in Paris. (I spared telling him that those were so miserably lit that they looked like mud.) His face fell, he did not have the means to go to Paris. Then I understood that by pictures like that he did not necessarily mean *Water Lilies* by Monet, but any pictures in which there shone the work and devotion and intellect of Man, not otherwise, as I soon learned, than we (Copernicus, Kepler, etc.) had whirled our moon in space.

"Oh, if that's what you mean! we have fifty great works of art right here in New York City!" I said proudly. "We have a few in this very museum." I steered him toward the *Three Musicians*. I urged him by no means to miss the Tlingit Blanket at the Museum of the American Indian, nor the Unicorn in the Cloisters, and there was an Easter Island head in Natural History, where he could also take in the dinosaurs on the top floor.

Jeremy was drunken on the display, the *proofs*, of the grandeur of mankind. He was insatiable for more and more and more, like a man who has been lost in a desert, endlessly thirsty and who ought not to drink so fast. I watched him sidelong. He was a borderline schizophrenic, all right, but I listened carefully to his syntax and I was pretty sure he wouldn't break down. He was glaringly using the monuments of our magnificence simply in order to ward off a catastrophic response to the newsy fact that we do not live in paradise. It certainly was going to persist as a fact, and he'd certainly have to keep hustling. But what gave me confidence for him was his beautiful serviceableness. He had come to the idea that if he did not find us lovely enough, he'd set about to make us lovely. I bowed to him.

We had coffee and sandwiches on the roof. I was ashamed how poor the food was, especially when he told me that he used to run a restaurant himself—I could imagine that it was a solid little restaurant. I was not personally ashamed at the ugly view of the mid-town street—it wasn't my fault; my brother and I have never stopped nagging for a Master Plan —but I was distressed at it for him.

"No no!" said Jeremy, "your city's immense. When you go round it in the steamboat. It's only when you get in the streets that it's no good."

"Ah, you took the boat ride!" I said, pleased, for my Hudson shows off well.

. . . "Look, Jeremy," I said finally, tentatively—I wanted to calm him down but not break his spirit— "Granted some of these pictures are wonderful—but you must bear in mind —that they are only works of art." Being an artist myself, I knew what that counted for. "Men are *good* at art-works. Other works too—bridges, and your rocket, and, you know, the Salk vaccine, the antibiotics, and all that jazz. Oh, when we have something to work at, we're first rate. You don't even need to get fancy: just look at the fellow seriously fixing his car, or two men working seriously on the same job. They're absorbed, cooperative; they're human. But it's quite a different matter, you know, if you're looking at the human animals themselves, in their lives, their purposes—especially if you *don't* have something to work at—do you follow me?"

"Living is no different from pictures," said Jeremy Owen. "You've got to work at it, and it's all by grace. It's there, but it's rare." He gave me his frank grin. He was sane as a hammer. "I see you're trying to calm me down but not break my spirit. Really, it's not necessary. Don't make allowances for me." He touched me with his hand. "Thanks. I like you," said Jeremy Owen.

11.

The youths hanging around the corners made him uneasy. They existed in his home town too, who could not find work and also did not want to, but they were few and each one seemed to be a special case ultimately dissoluble by friendly heckling or somebody's giving him a job willy-nilly—or by their leaving town. With a start Jeremy realized that the youngsters who left town came to New York.

In New York these young men were not special cases. They formed a class in the city, with their own class properties of disaffection, degeneration of skills, drinking, drugs, and finally their own literature.

Indeed, the discovery of classes, classes of people with characteristic troubles, was the most surprising experience that Jeremy Owen had in his visit to New York. In New York there were so many people. Back home, he was aware of personal problems; here overnight, for he was quick, he became a psychologist and a sociologist. But whereas formerly he would have thought that this new way of having his problems, as universal in the nature of things, would make them abstract and impersonal; to his amazement he found that, on the contrary, they became even more grindingly personal, intransigeant, hard. And if you could confront them, noble.

Ignorant himself, he was appalled by the ignorance of these youths. They had never noticed that there were tides in the Hudson River, not to speak of knowing the causes of tides. They did not know who the Mayor was. They did not know the principle of an electric motor. They could not fix a bicycle.

On the corner of the street he lived on, hung out a gang of Puerto Rican lads. One of them came with a shining new bicycle and all were soon wildly pedalling it. Jeremy was charmed by this generous camaraderie, as if all property belonged to all. But he quickly saw that there *was* no community, no mutual pleasure or mutual concern, but each one was simply proving his prowess and demanding an equal go in order not to be belittled. All were so fearful of everything that they could not afford to be affectionate to any one. Soon there was a crash; a few spokes of the bike were broken, and the wheel knocked out of line. The fellows formed a circle around the accident and looked at it a moment. The owner angrily kicked the rider, a smaller boy, who was hurt. "*Perdida—*" they said, and went away leaving the bicycle and the hurt boy in the gutter.

Jeremy was at a loss. The bicycle was lying there. He began to call them back—he would show them how to fix it, fix it for them. But he pulled up short as if some one had caught him by the shoulder in an iron grip. He was *not* to be the feeder of the multitude. He was *not* to be their bicycle repairman.

But the bicycle was lying there. It was shining, it was brand new, it was as beautiful as a bicycle. The hurt boy was sitting on the curb rubbing his knee. Jeremy looked at this and looked at that. "I'd take the bike myself," he thought, "but what do I need with a bicycle? Is the boy badly hurt? Am I his nurse?"

He wished that he had some special talent that he had to exercise—the "talent that is death to hide," as Milton said; or that some problem of the world, not his problem, puzzled and intrigued him, so that he could work at it; or that, as some did, he took satisfaction in pleasing himself. Then he could evade this dilemma of either having to work in conditions not interesting to a man, or of having no job at all. It was a general dilemma, for they were surplus. In 1957, nobody desperately needed you or me.

None of his wishes was true; he had no special talent, no special interest, nor urge to please himself. His disposition was not assertive but serviceable. But he had a balky strain that said, "I won't."

He touched the abandoned bicycle with the toe of his shoe. At this moment Jeremy Owen would have put his fist through a wall. . . . He turned away.

Quick as a flash, nimble as could be, as soon as his back was turned, the hurt boy had leaped up and dragged the bicycle into a basement. Jeremy caught it out of the corner of his eye and he was enchanted. All problems were solved! The boy at least *wanted* the bicycle!

His mood swung to the euphoric as he continued his walk up the street. He looked back and there, where there had been a hurt boy and an abandoned bicycle, now was nothing at all, the empty street. Jeremy laughed with pleasure, it was so dandy.

12.

On his own stoop was Julia sitting, smoking a cigarette, wearing a red bell-hop's cap, a black velvet jacket, and a skirt of the yellow plaid of her clan. She had been watching him as he watched, and she was pleased that he was enjoying it.

He started. "You've been watching me down the block," he said, "and you seem to be pleased that I was enjoying it."

"Yes," she admitted.

"That's remarkable, for you to be pleased at that."

Nevertheless, he felt that he ought to be severe, for obviously it would not do for her to come pursuing him, as she had done. Why it would not do, was not clear to him. "Why have you followed me here?" he said severely. "Explain yourself. I said No, I wouldn't bring you to New York."

"You didn't bring me, I came after you," she said simply. "When you left, there was no use my staying behind. I came as soon as I got paid."

"And what are you going to do if I don't want you here?" he said brutally, wondering at his words, for he was, rather, sexually aroused as he looked at her; he wanted to touch her and was complacent about not having to sleep alone again that night.

"I don't think that's likely," she said bravely, or maybe simply, for his look was evident. "Unless you try hard against it—like a sailor on the town—it's impossible not to like the woman you enjoy yourself with."

"What the devil do you know about sailors on the town!" he said, amused.

"I figure it this way," she said. "Before I left, I figured it out. Either he'll have me around—from time to time—" Her eyes moistened. "Or he—you—won't—in which case I'm no worse off anyway—without. Isn't that logical?" She could not smile.

He sat down beside her on the step and put an arm around her waist. Dutifully to himself, he went over her long speech, how and why she came, what she thought likely, and how she figured. No matter which way he turned it, her argument made lovely sense.

"What are you thinking?" she said.

"I am turning what you say this way and that."

"Ah, you are twisting it and turning it!" She bit her lips.

"No, I'm not twisting it," he said, surprised but not indignant. "Come upstairs, Julie. Have you eaten?"

13.

Jeremy had never read the play *Everyman*, nor had it been played in his town. But he knew the name *Everyman*, although he imagined, somewhat off the mark, that it was a story of every man's life rather than his death. Now being in New York, where there were so many people, he was powerfully seized by the dramatic idea of the fate that belonged to Everyman. Not the luck or bad luck, the talent or beauty or only average gifts, or the stupidity or ugliness, that mark this man as different from that man, but those facts of life which happen to Everyman, so that every man would say that you were talking about *him*. Likely that would be a melancholy story, for by and large one did not see mankind cutting a glorious figure in New York City, winter of 1957.

"Where are you going, Everyman?" said Jeremy, to the man who was going but who was willing to stay a moment and exchange the time of day.

"Looking for a job," said Everyman.

"Yes, everybody's got to do something," said Jeremy. "*I* seem to be conducting a Public Opinion Survey. What kind of work do *you* want to do?"

"I beg your pardon?"

"What do you like? what are you good at? since you say you're looking for a job."

"I don't think you size up the situation, stranger," said Everyman. "You sound like from up in the mountains. Around here, there *aren't* many jobs that are fit for a man to do, and if you want to get anything at all, you'd better omit that kind of thinking, I mean what you like and what you're good at. Once in a blue moon you'll find a man here doing what suits him; but he ain't Everyman."

"Do you mean that Everyman is spending his working life doing what's no good?"

"That's right. Forty years, forty hour week."

"Hm. . . . What's the matter, Everyman?"

"Well, to be frank with you, I'm lonely."

"Ah, you mean you don't have enough sex? I've heard about that."

"*You* are frank. No, I didn't mean that. But that too. I don't think you'll find many in New York as get enough as is good for them. But what I meant was just lonely. I don't love anybody. I don't feel that they love me, though I guess I may be wrong. You ever been in love?"

"I don't think so," said Jeremy. "But leave me out of this."

"I been in love, a few times. And whenever I was in love, it didn't work out. The damnedest thing. This one didn't happen to like me; another one, her brother beat the tar out of her and I had to stand by; another one the father beat the tar out of *me*. Another one, my furlough was up and afterward she had made other arrangements. Oh, nothing unusual, just what happens to Everyman. But do you know what it adds up to?"

"What does it add up to, Everyman?"

"Since I never been able to get this simple thing I want when I want it, I've become convinced that the world isn't ordered for the best. Now that saps your confidence. There are lots of things possible to people who have been lucky in love that are impossible to me because I have no faith. If God couldn't provide better for such a simple thing, that terrific want and need of mine sometime—well, I don't know."

"Don't you believe in God, Everyman?"

"I don't know. I tell you, I don't know. That's one of the things you'll learn if you go around questioning Everyman, that I'm ignorant. I don't know the first things. What to teach my children, nor how to get them to learn it if I knew. I don't know how to fix the machines I use every day. They get me in wars, but how in hell should I know what's it about? It's too big and far. (By the way, they don't know either; what's in the papers is bullshit.) Naturally I can't live this way, continually confused; so soon I know all about everything, it's all in the papers. Especially if you're a New York like Everyman, we're notorious for it. Do *you* know anything?" he asked curiously.

Jeremy pondered it a moment. "I've just begun," he said carefully. "I think I have learned a few *small* things."

"Will you tell me?" said Everyman eagerly, "and be my guide? and be my best man by my side?"

"When I am more sure of myself, Everyman. I swear it," said Jeremy.

"Well, I'm not getting any younger," said Everyman, and they walked along in silence.

"Why are you limping, Everyman?"

"Cause I'm lame, stupid. Had an accident as a child."

"Oh, that was tough luck."

"Tough luck? No, not at all. It's in the nature of things. Everybody's got something."

"Really? Isn't that exaggerated?" said Jeremy.

"How! exaggerated! Open your eyes, man. One has migraine, one has ulcers. They're all chronics. This one's alcoholic, this one's queer, and this one's what they call a psychopathic personality and lands in jail. Some of 'em can't get it up and more than 50 per cent of the women are frigid. The average children are stuck with their parents, and the orphans and foundlings grow up with cold feelings. Just figure it out, man. If there's two per cent of this and five per cent of that and three and a half per cent of the other, it soon adds up to a whopping hundred and eighty-eight per cent of the whole jolly population. Do you mean to tell me there's nothing wrong with *you?* You're a liar! *I'm* one of the lucky ones!" boasted Everyman, "I'm just lame. I can work and walk,

even if I won't run no mile in three fifty like an Australian. I
grant you," he said morosely, "we're not very interesting—the
ailing and neurotic—they never surprise you. But nobody is
to blame! No—one—is—to—blame. We're just not made for
this world. As if they sent us to the wrong planet. You take
it easy, buddy."

And Everyman went off, raucously singing *The Ballad of
the Hurricane:*

> When you was little, man, your mama
>   threw out the baby with the bath,
> you ain't got the equipment
>   to beat your feet and laugh.
>
> So sit down there and drink your beer
>   and don't be bothering
> the people drinking with their friends
>   so gay and good-looking.
>
> Don't snap out of it, buddy,
>   stay with it till it hurts,
> because you only live once
>   you might as well know the worst.
>
> No, look, he said, my situation
>   is delicate. He frowned.
> I gotta stay here in the center
>   o all these winds rushin around,
>
> a hundred twenty miles an hour
>   around the edges, knock you silly,
> where here I'm just as calm as calm
>   and the sky is sunny.

He bowed to Fate, and a mile an hour
   he drifted out the door northwest
by the compass that he wore
   dangling from his vest.

That was the blast that wrecked my house
   and knocked the spire off Old North Church,
it drowned a man in Providence
   and left New London in the lurch.

Mighty trees with dirty roots
   were floating in Narragansett Bay
with chickens roosting in the leaves
   at the break of day.

After that flood at daybreak
   our town was dirty and washed
and we walked the streets in wonder
   to look at what was smashed.

14.

"Are you still questioning Everyman, Everyman?" I said
to Jeremy.

He nodded dumbly.

"What did he tell you this time?"

"That Everyman has no real job and no faith, lousy sex,
and he's ignorant and crippled."

"Oh?"

"And he went off singing about a drunk who thought he
was a Hurricane, and he was."

"Yes. *The Ballad of the Hurricane.*"

"But I have hammered out of it a slogan!" said Jeremy passionately, and the sweat rolled off his face as if he were literally hammering a tough metal. "Foster Excellence! Approve of it, even if it hurts, and give it chances to be used. I came here to learn something to tell him, and I've already found one thing."

II

THREE COMMUNITY PIECES

A VISIT TO CHARTRES

1.

I did want to go and see the Cathedral of Chartres, even though with the dispiritment with which I want anything these days. I did want to; the proof is that I was not two days in France but I and my companion were driving the road to Chartres.

When we were a few kilometers past Ablis—and still I had no hot eagerness to arrive—I chanced to lift my eyes to the horizon, across the long rolling green plain. Far off, ghostly in the haze, were the well-known unlike towers of the Cathedral of Chartres, beyond the horizon, half an inch high, hovering in the haze. I, to my surprise, turned pale and flushed, and my heart was pounding.

But we sped on our way (Route 188) and when next the

Cathedral flashed into view, she was clear to see and a neat size like a picture, she was "pretty as a picture" and very like a picture of the Cathedral of Chartres. It was a remarkable illusion, for there was the Cathedral of Chartres but there was no town of Chartres. I could not help smiling at how cunningly and skillfully that building put herself on display.

I had been moved and charmed and alas! (I knew myself) these feelings—these feelings plus my usual effortful and earnest enough aesthetic and sociological reflections—would be the height of my joy in the Cathedral of Chartres. I felt I had had it, and I might just as well turn around right then and go away.

But a car drives on and when next I saw her—we were nearly in Chartres—now only the upper parts of the building on the hilltop were visible, girt and obstructed by her clustering houses. "Naturally, it is the Cathedral of the *town*—," I thought; I was already embarked on my usual effortful aesthetic and sociological reflections. But there was a very ugly warehouse in the foreground, in the wrong century, in the wrong color, and hogging the view. "They really should take that one out of the way," I said to my companion in my usual impractically helpful manner.

In Chartres, the Cathedral on her hill was lost from view. We took a wrong turning and we were out of the town. We circled back. We had to ask our way, and to go up an improbable hill, and through a back alley. But it was in the nature of the case (everything that is is in the nature of the case), for any community-square of those times would be enclosed and not directly approachable.

118

Sure enough! There, up the little alley, *was* the Cathedral of Chartres, on the square.

The square was not commodious enough, of course. Of course.

2.

Of course I was content with my immediate cursory inspection of the Cathedral of Chartres, for it was the Cathedral of Chartres and I am not a fool. I was far from disappointed. I was a little bit surprised. It happens that I had expected the surface to be more austere, but the exterior texture, the worn, worn texture, was like a precious stone.

Yes, I walked about her and again and again she forced from me a smirk of satisfaction and a grunt of approval. The great transept portico, and the older tower. I was glad, I was satisfied, that I had not turned around and gone away without coming to see the Cathedral of Chartres.

I went inside to see if there was something amiss, but there was nothing amiss. The chairs and the electric lights were easy to think away. A few of the windows were missing. At the transept, if you looked into the choir, the big round columns were manly and lovely. How big and manly! If you went around the apse and looked back behind you, you would not be displeased. And when you stood on the stage and looked into the nave, then the auditorium was dark and the high rose shone, not brightly, close in your eyes.

There was no sun that day and the color was not gorgeous, but you could easily see that the color would be gorgeous at the hour that it would be gorgeous. I am uninstructed, and I could not read the hundreds of pictures in the windows, but I had no doubt at all that, if I could, they'd be surprisingly appropriate and profoundly thought-provoking to a careful aesthetic and sociological reflection—but I was content enough as it was, to the degree that I am content with anything these days.

Nevertheless, I kept looking curiously up at the small gallery. Couldn't I get up there? And how could I get up there? to whom did one appeal? I am childish and I like to climb around on these buildings. There were many sightseers, but nobody was up there.

3.

I weep easily when there is something beautiful—especially if there is no way to get closer by clambering on. (Thwarted, I weep instead of getting angry.) And by now my tiny smiles and grunts had given way to a few tiny gleams of tears. These tears were certainly tears for paradise lost, for when something is beautiful it is a reminder of paradise lost. But also—I am beginning to understand it—they were tears of hurt feelings. My feelings are hurt because they have left me out. This beautiful world, and my life is not so beautiful: they have left me out. Why has He left me out? Am I not as loyal a son as the next? I *am* a loyal son! But no doubt He is a loving father, only He does not understand me and He treats me in a way that is *not* really good for me; it has gone on too long. Skip it.

Skip it. Today at the Cathedral of Chartres there was some kind of festival preparing. A large company of nuns and several troops of cub-scouts. Priests began to light the candles at the table and to shoo us nosybodies into the aisle. And certainly there was going to be a bishop. I had come on the right day to see my lovely in use! I didn't much care what it was about—although, of course! I know! if I made more effort to read the pictures and inform myself about the day's ceremony, I'd be richly rewarded. But I am tired.

I too was shooed into the aisle and, being in the aisle, I came by the door to the bell-tower, and there I saw posted the solemn warning:

WARNING
Ministry of Fine Arts

Visitors to the Upper Parts of the Monument
will proceed at their own risk.
The Ministry cannot be responsible in case
of accident.

Good! so it *was* possible to go aloft. That was for me. Something to do, to clamber. At once I entered at the narrow door and I began, two steps at a time, the circular ascent. By a hundred steps I was out of breath. It was dark.

4.

I began to be afraid. Let me explain about myself. I am an exceptionally fearful person but not timid. I mean, I don't hold back, I commit myself rapidly, often too rapidly, to a risk that happens to suggest itself; and not blindly, as if I didn't know it was a risk, but as if thoughtlessly, as if I didn't care about consequences. Yet then very soon I become afraid and, usually for no adequate reason, almost panicky. But I don't panic, that is I don't run away. (Although I *can* run away, if there's a real danger.)

However it was, now, climbing a public stairway, I became terribly afraid. It was that I was out of breath. On these circular stairs in the dark, where hundreds of thousands have ascended and descended in the dark, I was out of breath and almost in a panic. My thought was that I would never get to the top. There were maybe 300 steps, I did not know how many there were, I could not calm myself to calculate how many there must be—but my heart would fail and I would die in that lonely tower lost forever, where hundreds of thousands had climbed before me for a thousand years, and God grant as many will follow me after! I climbed on.

At this moment, when I was almost in panic for nothing, there did occur something that was terrifying and I backed against the stone wall in terror. For right next to me, nay inside the dark spiral, sounded a mighty noise. I backed against the wall astonished. I clung to the wall and the stone wall was trembling. My hair stood up on my scalp.

It was the bell. The counter-stroke struck.

With a cry I leapt up the last steps and under the sky. I clung to the balustrade.

The square and the town fell away beneath me and I reeled. And all of the bells leaped into clangorous and joyous life.

They clanged round about me, whichever way I turned,

deafening and delightful, till I held my hands over my ears
and appealed for mercy. I was happy for the first time in a
long time.

They say there are two things that frighten a child, loud
noises and the fear of falling. I was frightened and I was
certainly like a child. But it wasn't noises but the glorious
clangor of bells that is almost noise; and instead of falling,
I could safely see the far view from the tower of the Cathedral
of Chartres.

Over the bass of the big bells, the smaller bells began their
shrieking scales; and my eyes leapt near and far.

(The Cathedral square below was too small.)

I clambered about the roof, not unlike a tiny baby, who
plays not with the grown-ups, but on them. For she was like
La Géante of Baudelaire:

> "Parcourir à loisir ses magnifiques formes!
>   ramper sur le versant de ses genoux énormes!"

—I liked "to roam at my leisure on her magnificent shapes,
and to clamber on the slope of her enormous knees."

5.

There was a gentleman there, and his five-year-old boy.

"N'a-t-il pas peur?" I asked.

"Mais non, il n'a pas peur."

The small boy was confidently holding his papa's hand,
without clinging to it or clutching at it.

I never had a human father, and I loved this gentleman
and his brave boy.

But tiny below, the police were clearing the square. The shrieking scales ceased. The thunderous peals were abating.

Hurriedly I came down from the tower to see the service. And this time I took care to count the steps, in order to know at least one thing accurately in this world, but I lost count.

6.

The church that I emerged in was alive. In use.

Or it was that I had been touched in the body, as when somebody touches you intimately or slaps you across the face (it comes to the same thing), and from then on the situation is alive. Because I had been panicky in the narrow place, I emerged in the great nave trembling.

I didn't know what it was about, but surely it was a happy occasion and a joyous service, for each response of the choir succeeded in a brighter mode and a merrier rhythm. With vehement enthusiasm first the bishop and then the boys flung out their incense before them. The smoke was piercing sharp to the nostrils.

It was a short service; the procession of the nuns and the scout-uniformed kids was already beginning to form. The chant of the choir was loud and allegro.

The chanting was not excellent, but good enough. The organ took it up with a roar.

Naturally I pressed closer. *Naturally* my mouth was hanging open.

God pity me! My expectation was extreme.

Nay, I see that He does not misunderstand me, His loyal

boy. Simply that He can't, He doesn't have the material. *He is in pain too.*

For—what? Was it possible? Weren't all those people going to sing? Weren't they going to shout out and sing? All those several hundred nuns and troops of crystal-throated boy scouts? And the bishop creeping along under his palanquin? But what on earth else were they good for? They marched awkwardly past and did not open their mouths.

Some persons were throwing flowers, in the silence.

They didn't ring the bells.

7.

Now I began to be angry. My disappointment was profound. I was angry with my best, my indignant, anger that surges only when I have been a little happy and I see the world as it is. I was contemptuous of those dummies as they filed out in their well-behaved rows, during the festival of flowers, with never a peep out of them, even though the occasion and the place and the congregation had prepared for this moment the bellow of a thousand untrained voices singing the appropriate words, and also bells.

"What?" I asked myself coldly, "and didn't they *know* the appropriate words? Why not? Surely *I* don't know them, or I'd sing out if I was the only one." I am not timid to bear witness in such cases.

Or I put it this way: "If they didn't know the words—if you don't know the words, you dummies, and *therefore* are struck dumb, why don't you ask somebody to prepare you the words? There are two or three poets right here in France; or even me, for instance, though I am a stranger—" I am not unskilled at finding words for such occasions.

Or—God pity us! "If you don't even realize that at this moment there *ought* to be social words and a climax of song and bells, then by what right, how do you dare, to be marching in a procession from my Cathedral of Chartres?"

"God damn them all!" I said. Such prayers in my mouth are simply statements of how it is, they do not imply any ill wish. It is a way I have of saying that these, who should have broken into heaven, were effectually in hell; and I—I who had been trembling with hope for us all—was firm with rage, because I am in purgatory living here with these people.

> Saved! as I have faith
> and probable proof,
>   but O God, am I weary
>   of living in Purgatory,
>
> in pain and fire, tedious
> waiting for the Voice
>   of love that summons
>   and the voice that responds.

Perhaps I expect too much. That's what they tell me, that I expect too much. Do I expect too much? *What* do I expect? That at the just moment we people should come across. Is this much? Such things have happened.

I stood there in the Cathedral, feeling strong emotions. Coursing through me, also, was a current of vitality. I was astonished and pleased at myself that I did not burst into tears. I had no hurt feelings. I was secure in my anger, for in the end in these matters I do know better, ignorant though I am.

They had filed past me and the floor was strewn with the petals of peonies. And oh Lord, what a waste!

8.

Softly.

Softly. A little patience. For look at my darling, how patiently *she* houses us, native fools and tourists. She comes across and gives herself, with nothing amiss. She is still so much there that our later errors are easy to think away. She thereby gives an honest poet also the occasion to vent his anger without hurt feelings. That's a great gift she gives, my darling. (That's a great gift thee gives me, darling.) I'm grateful for this beauty that has led me to present anger instead of as usual to the gleam of tears for paradise lost. This beauty that has led me to smiles, for by damn! isn't she lovely? Now that the bishop has crept out of the way under his idiotic palanquin.

I mean, it's not necessary to make allowances for the Cathedral of Chartres; *isn't* she lovely?

9.

I went outside where my companion was waiting for me in the car. He set the motor going. "I'm sorry I've been so long,"

I said, "but I'll be back in just a minute—" and I wandered as if aimlessly away, though I had a plan.

I wandered down the alley on the south, ostentatiously examining how the square tower of the Cathedral of Chartres mounts into its octagonal spire, something I had already examined to my satisfaction, but I was embarrassed and secretive for what I was about, and there were still a few loiterers. They left.

Swiftly I leapt up three or four steps of the portico, to where there was a fine little block in the limestone wall, to kiss, a good adequate sample of that worn and tender rock, to touch lightly and kiss.

Shyly I kissed the dumb stone with a little peck of a kiss. I was thinking, in a swift whisper, "There, I love thee; thee'll see. I'll come back often when there's more opportunity. Thee'll see how I am, faithful, whatever they say and think; once I'm in love I never change. (I'll write thee a poem when I'm away, no?) I seem to be so sour and hard to please always, and it's true enough; but I do love thee, thee is so lovely. Also so practical. It rarely goes together. Darling, good-bye. I'm sorry about the others."

I went back to the car and climbed in. He started the motor.

There was no denying it, the Cathedral square was not adequate for a good view of the Cathedral.

My companion said, "Well, did you find out what the procession was about?"

"Solstice. They celebrate it as a Fête of Flowers."

"Yes, they were throwing a lot of flowers."

I thought then, as I still think, if He is in pain too, my

father, I ought to put on a bright face, to make Him more easy.

Yet here I am, cramped, oppressed, and uneasy almost to anguish because the Cathedral of Chartres' square is too small. Or alternatively—if the houses of the town of Chartres would cluster closer up to their Cathedral, and do without the square altogether. Creator Spirit, wouldn't either way do well for the Cathedral of Chartres? So I turn it and ask myself. I am absurd; my face is drawn with pain all day for what I cannot remedy.

A SENIOR CONCERT OF THE HIGH
SCHOOL OF MUSIC AND ART

It's a big orchestra of empty chairs, with their stands and lights and music-sheets. Eighty-five places. Only the drummer is there, a slight bespectacled boy with colorless hair; when he bends his ear close to the kettledrums, he is lost in the equipment. He has stage fright and is nervously banging away bang! bong! dominant and tonic. Suddenly other players are appearing at their stands, trying to look business-like. A young miss, quite a young lady with a turquoise blouse and a skirt of flaring orange, is screwing together with quick twists the three pieces of her silver flute.

The kids have collected too early, to warm up their instruments. They have stage fright and each is private. Each kid is practicing his own phrase fortissimo, the din is fierce.

Each kid heedless of the others and of the audience that has begun straggling in, the parents.

You expect them to start pacing up and down on the field, to burst into a sprint down the field, to heave a lead shot erratically in a thoughtless direction and knock somebody's head off, while the sun floods down his unstinting light from the royal blue.

Now thirty or forty of them have gathered and seem to be busy practicing. But if you look at the program—the phrases they are loudly playing have nothing to do with the concert to come. In private, each kid is seeking safety in his "own" music, the way musical adolescents—and these adolescents are very musical—hear with fanatical rapture the harmony that was invented especially for oneself, no one else in all the generations ever understood it, "really" understood it. Also, without any stage fright in his isolated daydream, each is performing brilliantly on a bright stage to a vast audience, with universal admiration, triumphant over envious enemies who are magnanimously forgiven (that's the best part of it).

So one lad with a brass trumpet is exclaiming *Freedom! Freedom!* from *Fidelio.* And another with an ear-splitting horn is boasting that he is Siegfried.

It is not embarrassing because they are not embarrassed; but one is abashed for them, they are so young and exposed; but they are not abashed.

A slide trombone has acquired a hat over his bell, and he is taking with an arrogant posture the chorus of a Dixie blues, but when he ends with a flourish, crazy, man! and gives it to his buddy—alas! the clarinet is brooding with the aged Brahms who has been reading Sophocles. Unconscious of everything, the young lady with the silver flute is discoursing earnestly with the Blessed Spirits. And the little drummer is banging away at the march from the *Symphonie Pathétique,* streamed round by the flapping banners of the United Nations and bawling out the melody. But you cannot hear anything in the din.

Next moment, silence. The house is full, the kids are poised, their conductor has stepped onto the podium and raps. The stage-curtain parts revealing the choir—so *there* are the rest of the seniors!—and they have begun *Wachet auf!*

The orchestra has begun to play and I am blind with tears.

But what's to weep about any of this? Naturally they play well, they are very musical kids. Naturally they play well together, they are well rehearsed and they know one another. The conducting is simple and sensible, firm on the broad lines and on the obvious dynamics. There is plenty of spirit, it is *animal* spirit. The nobility—there is nobility—comes from the pride and aspiration of many poor cultured homes. All this is natural and to be expected; why then should tears be streaming down my cheeks and I cannot see anything but a bright sheet of light?

Because it is our orchestra.

Always it is absence and loss that we weep for; when we seem to be weeping for joy, we are weeping for paradise lost. And the case is—as I look about in our community and remember the longing of our lives and the frustration of our longing—the case is that we do not have any orchestra. This is a truth too bitter to live with and we usually dismiss it and keep our faces set as best we can.

But here is our orchestra! It is playing *Wachet auf!* Our

133

choir is taking it up. With the opening of this new possibility, at once the old tears well and roll down our cheeks. Our mouths are open, breathing in and out.

This orchestra is proud of its orchestra. The adolescents take it for granted that on the occasion they can rely on one another.

I sympathize with the conductor who is a man of my own age. He is smirking and continually breaking into smiles and broad grins. Each time they have traversed a hard passage, he breaks into a broad grin as if to say, "Listen, hey? the way they got through that! I told you they could! I promised you they would!" But the young people are playing right on. They are neither smirking nor nervous nor grimly determined, just matter-of-factly playing the music that they think is just beautiful, and indeed it is very grand and beautiful. They are attentive to the music, but they are also damned proud of their orchestra.

The girls' voices ring out loud and bright. The young tenors and basses do not have an equal weight; you would say that the young men are not confident, they are afraid their voices will break. Boys! risk it! give forth! (the conductor is pleading with his shaking left hand)—what is the use of young male voices if they do not shout out loud and clear? There, that's better. It doesn't matter if a few break down when there are so many brothers supporting.

We are towards the end of May. The school concert is part of the commencement exercises, a demonstration of the work of the year, of the four years. *Wachet auf! wachet auf!* This is not the "own" music of any of those kids, I suppose, but they have chosen it for us, and do they not take it well upon themselves! They are reconciled to us (us at our best, to be sure); they agree to continue. It is their commencement. I wish that they were in fact beginning into such a community as they seem so well able to take upon themselves.

The scene is clear and sharp. *"Thou art That!"* What does it mean? The immortal humanity. Each one stands as a witness.

As sometimes happens when you have been surprisingly moved and are thereby *in* the scene, some object spontaneously brightens and stands out from the background; or first one, then another, then another. A spotlight falling across one face, another face shining out of an unique shadow. Like those group photographs in the biographies of famous men, where the face of the hero as a boy seems to shine out from the group, destined for his career, although when the picture was taken all the faces were equal.

Before, they were all isolated in their jarring soliloquies, pathetic, violent, promissory adolescents. But now one, two, and three heads loom alone—doomed to it—as witnesses of immortal humanity.

The red-headed boy in the shaft of light has been doomed to sing in a new way; you can see the guilt and suffering of his absolute break with the generations on his stubborn and imploring face. He is begging for us to listen to him, but stubborn to persist in his way whether we will or not. And why should we pay attention to him when he has broken with us? But also both he and we know that there has been no break at all; we are laughing about it underneath, at the same time as we are set on making one another very unhappy.

Notice, too, the face of that serious little girl in the shadow. She is cursed with an eerie and unerring intuition that frightens her teachers and makes her classmates freeze. In self-protection and protection of the others, she hides her truth behind clever words, she is a smart aleck. No one likes her, but every one is going to need her. She weeps a good deal because the boys do not make love to her and the girls don't invite her to their parties. She would like to be like the others, but she cannot, by willing it, be stupider than she is.

That dark lad in the choir whose voice, among so many, rings pure and clear right to my ears: why is he frowning? He is a forlorn angel. He is not one of the fallen angels, for he has a passport into paradise; but he seems to be lost in a woods, his wings bedraggled. His trouble is that he persists in wanting to bring us home with him, and we will not go along. He invites us, we start to go with him, and he is elated; then he finds we have deserted him, and he frowns. He has courage.

Creator spirit, prosper us. *Wachet auf!* they are thundering the chorale.

A STATUE OF GOLDSMITH

1.

I spent a couple of months in rainy Dublin, lonely and malcontent as elsewhere. For I contrive, often with ingenuity and boldly seizing opportunities, to get into a situation where I can be alone and do as I please, and then I am lonely and "doing as I please" does not get me what I want. Yet while I was in Dublin I finished work on a fine book that often touched me deeply and moved me to love and admiration for itself, so that when I had indeed finished the last sentence I fell on my knees, and prayed that my book would have an easy access and an understanding reception in the world.

During the lonely days and nights when I was not doing that work, however, I tried, as I do, to make human connections of friendship in Dublin, rarely getting anywhere, often let down, and fearful of the consequences of such inappropriate connections as I did make. I am very inept. It is not interesting to report it.

My favorite haunting—for I love rivers, and ships and trucks, and to watch the heavy work of loading and unloading cargoes—was to go along the Liffey and try to mix with the stevedores and sailors. I guess I was in love with a crew of workmen at the far end, who were dismantling for scrap-iron the ancient freighter *Kyleglen*. The scrap is important for the Irish, since they have no native iron of their own; it was a big and useful job.

Of the half-dozen, with their torches and their crane, one was a grand workman. I gazed at him with an aching heart. He had a plain open smiling face and a tall straight easy bearing every pose of which was graceful; but he was not so beautiful off the job—at lunch, playing soccer as they did with a small rubber ball—as when he was working.

His name was Jerry. When Jerry leaned on the crowbar, the mass moved, even though the others could not budge it. When he gave a smash with the stone mallet, the object broke, though the others had hacked in vain. He was perhaps stronger than the others in a lithe way, but it was more that he knew what he was doing; he had the confidence and follow-through that come from paying attention. If there was a task that was out of the routine and either more delicate or difficult, they spontaneously drew back and let Jerry do it. He knew the job even too well for the job—he knew more than the foreman—although it was big and dangerous work. There was a pathos in his excellence.

"You know," I said to him during a cigarette, "you're a grand workman."

"You mean, I work hard?" He didn't especially.

"No, not at all. I mean you know what you're doing. You're better than the others—and it shows. I just wanted to tell you how it looks from outside." The fact is that I love to praise, and to have something to praise.

He lowered his face and blushed. "Some of them *will* get themselves killed sooner or later" was his comment.

Of course I wished he would be interested in me too, but he always politely contrived to move away from me, as if chary of me. The boundary of education and so forth that meant nothing to me meant a lot to them.

I watched them with longing: how the iron obstacles that thwart us, *they* cut through with their acetylene torches.

And it would begin to rain again and they would go below, leaving me forlorn on the dock. In love with the crew of wreckers dismantling the *Kyleglen*, but what kind of thing was that to be in love with?

I walked away from there back into the city and I thought to visit Trinity Library and see the famous Book of Kells, and I entered the University close between the statues of Burke and Goldsmith.

2.

Once up in the long hall of the Library, I soon began to hum and breathe deeply as I do when there are interesting things to see, passing from shelf to shelf and showcase to showcase. The ancient vellum books were of course remarkable, but it was the display and honor accorded to our authors that absorbed my attention. I was pleased by the judicious evaluation of Goldsmith:

> "He went to Trinity College and after graduation tried to make a living in various ways without success. As a hack writer he produced a large number of works on subjects of which he knew little. His literary reputation, however, rests securely on *The Vicar of Wakefield*, *The Deserted Village*, and his play *She Stoops to Conquer*, one of the great comedies of the English theatre."

The school-grades of Jonathan Swift for 1685: Natural Philosophy *Male*, Greek and Latin *Bene*, Theme *Negligenter*. Samuel Lover's *Handy Andy*. And I was interested to notice that Bernard Shaw's handwriting was as tiny and unbroken as my own, with bold descents below the line; of course marching on with fuller and more regular impulse than mine; but with a tell-tale leftward slant of holding back. That is, our manuscripts were comparable, with different prizes to be given to each; and he had already reaped his reward and I was going to win mine.

They had on show many an Irish novelist of no great merit, yet it was a fine thing to see honor done to them all in this hall of scholarship, by a people that has always esteemed wit and learning and daring eloquence, despite the appalling bigotry and censorship that they are subject to.

I spent a couple of hours, I guess, swiftly taking in and

musing on all these things—and the harp of Brian Boru—
during which time I did not think whether or not I was
happy. Having seen enough, I went out with a nod at the
armorial bearings of Elizabeth preserved from the original
buildings of the College, long since destroyed.

3.

As I came out of the Library, I think it was the sight of the
statue of Lecky seated, that set me off into a jolly mood. It
was so surprising to see a statue of Lecky, and there he was,
boots and side-whiskers, with a solemn face about to break
into a grin. Really very good.

However it was, as I looked about at the close, where the
young ones were hurrying to their classes on the hour, at
that moment I felt completely, alarmingly, *finally* at home
in Trinity College, Dublin. I didn't know a soul here, yet my
loneliness dropped from me as if it could never return. Knowing nobody made no difference, since I securely belonged to
the inner company of these authors, scholars, and doctors,
and I needed only to reveal myself, so to speak, to be welcome. My doctorate was a sound one, through (I think) Yale
and Cambridge back to Paris; likely they had my thesis somewhere on their shelves; and I had the prerogative to go into
one of those classes and join in the disputation. Nor would
I have disputed, but rather supported and underscored what
the professor was trying to tell them, for our company are
trustworthy on our home grounds.

Trinity was a university after my own size. Its tradition and slightly ragged Irish spirit were after my own style. (Nowhere except in Ireland have I ever felt appropriately dressed, neither too shabby nor too careful.) It did not hurt, either, that I have always found Irish young people the most attractive; they have been my type since childhood. And they were set off by a good sprinkling of Nigerians, Thailanders, Jews.

Here came a professor with his satchel of books, a burly man in a hurry. He looked confident of himself but short-tempered because of the chances of life, not enough time for lunch. I was just as glad that it was he and not I who had to get to that class.

I stood in the angle of the archway and lit my pipe and enjoyed my solitary anonymity in that square where I was most at home. Obviously it was there that it was right, and fated, for me to be in love, except that therefore there was no need for me to be in love at all or to feel any particular emotion whatever, except as a particular occasion might call for it. Yet I must have been a striking figure standing at my ease there, solitary, alertly watching, drawing on my pipe, for many of the kids who passed looked at me with curiosity in which there seemed to be respect.

The next moment I began again to feel my loneliness, my placelessness, my inactivity; the impossibility of everything I wanted in the world; how my natural spirits and health were in ruins and the hour about to strike. And, as if beaten in a battle and evacuating the fort, I went out through the archway worse off than I had come in. Between Burke and Goldsmith.

4.

Now it was in these circumstances that I came, that afternoon, to pose myself the question: *What is the meaning of this statue of Goldsmith? Why have they put it here?*

For as I emerged from the archway, there stood the statue of Goldsmith on my left hand. The pose relaxed but about to move; his right arm slightly retracted and with a pen for a weapon, about to stab at the book that he is holding in his left; a sweet Irish face and beginning to lose his hair.

That metal man: what connection did he have with Goldsmith who was dead? None whatever. How did Goldsmith who used to be alive, as I felt myself alive (and perhaps not with any happier feeling about it than I had), how did that Goldsmith survive in this bronze statue of Goldsmith? In no way whatever. This statue was present with us. A living Goldsmith was in no way present with us.

But no doubt it was just this that people were unwilling to tolerate, that the man whose relics were important to them, touched them even closely to laughter and tears and insight, should in no way be really here. Such a thing is eerie, it makes us anxious. Therefore, to alleviate their own unease, people erected a statue of Goldsmith and wrote on the pedestal "Goldsmith." But this did not immortalize Goldsmith; it did not do *anything* for Goldsmith.

But popular philosophers will speak of the man living on in our hearts, in our thoughts, in the influence of his works; we live in our culture and Goldsmith is our culture. Such philosophers seem to envisage a kind of shadowy mental and social immortality for the poet: and then that bronze figure (as one passed by) was a symbol, a memento, to call up such associations and influences and make the "immortal Goldsmith" glow with a little more substance: Goldsmith literally a figure in the living culture. This has been argued, and oh, I suppose there is something in it; namely, very little.

For as I stood there and thought of gone Goldsmith and thought of myself, it did not seem to me that, in my case, my existence as an object or influence for other people, added much to *my* life at all. Quite the contrary; in the instances where my words or deeds were for the good, I felt diminished by them rather than enhanced—*they* were not myself—they occurred as if on their own, though at the expense of myself; and in them I had no grounds of pride or satisfaction. When I had finished a work, I felt that much more exhausted, even though it was not I who made the work. And so far as my things worked in other people and gave them something useful, those people by no means responded by giving anything to me; rather, moved by the poem, they envied its author, and certainly no one stretched a hand to relieve my animal distress. I doubted that it was very different with Goldsmith. I would (now) have loved him and felt sorry for him, but he was dead.

Then what did they mean to be doing when they erected the statue of Goldsmith? Was it merely for guilt that they had not enough loved Goldsmith?

5.

These were bitter thoughts I had as I looked up at the statue of Goldsmith springing out of the green grass of Ireland; but at least they were natural thoughts. But when the true answer came to me, it froze my soul, for it was not even natural.

It was so simple. They put up the statue of Goldsmith in order to have a statue. Like a clench of the fist. Just for the immortality of it.

Not *his* immortality, nor even theirs; it was more abstract than that.

Nothing to do with Goldsmith. Or rather, they made their statue as an effigy of Goldsmith, taking his name and inventing an unlikely pose, not otherwise than a painter who is making a painting pretends to be painting a landscape with figures, but he is really making a painting. They wanted a statue and they took advantage of Goldsmith, after his death just as during his life, except that now at least it did him no harm.

Good; they had their statue; oh, and it was immortal like the Emperor of China "who never died because he never lived."

Nevertheless it was a statue of Goldsmith, and served him right! for it was Goldsmith first who taught them to take advantage of Goldsmith. Just for the immortality of it. Like a clench of the fist. *He* willed it. Because it was not from nothing, it was from the martyrdom of Goldsmith, that "his literary reputation rests securely on *The Vicar of Wakefield,*

The Deserted Village, and his play *She Stoops to Conquer,* one of the great comedies of the English theatre." The play was certainly his; it was written by Goldsmith who was dead. But *whose* literary reputation is it that "rests" so securely in that present tense? The statue of Goldsmith!

And suddenly the horror swept over me, and froze my soul, of those lonely months that I had spent working in rainy Dublin (in Florence, in Paris, in New York); and the horror of this frightful day that I was even now spending like a ghoul of immortality. Every part of it was chilling. How I loved to praise, and to have something to praise—just because I could not tolerate the common waste and death. (But the young workman was instinctively chary of me.) And I thought of us ghouls in the University close, who passed on our culture, just for the immortality of it. Like a clench of the fist. Like the statue of Goldsmith.

My animal spirit has left me; I am without lust; I could be pushed this way or that way or just left to lie; and with detachment I remember how I fell to my knees and prayed that a book I wrote would have an easy access and an understanding reception in the world.

III

MYTHS

III

THE DEATH OF AESCULAPIUS

1.

These are my memories of the death of Aesculapius our teacher.

When Diana the virgin huntress came keening, tearing her hair for Hippolytus, "You virgin!" said our teacher with icy contempt. "How do you dare ask for help from the physician of nature? Yet come," he said to us, "since we have sworn the oath."

When our teacher Aesculapius demonstrated the corpse of Hippolytus he was filled with passionate resentment. When we asked why he was angry, he lied and said, "I am not angry."

He said, "This is an unfinished situation. I shall revive Hippolytus. (But me, me I cannot revive.)"

He began as always with a description, absorbing soul from the environment. "You see, the day along the shore is bright. The regular waves are falling no louder than a conversational voice, and the offshore islands are showing in detail. In a billow of sand, here is the billow, the young horseman has come up the beach; he looses an arrow at the starting goose and misses. Here is the arrow. There is the goose in heaven. Where is the horse? There in the dunes. Why has he missed? Because he is disturbed, and his habit has been to hunt the game calmly, the attentiveness pouring from his eyes and from his hands that do not miss. Such is the so-called chaste love of Diana." But when Aesculapius mentioned Diana the virgin his voice was icy with contempt.

"Look! Quick as it rose the extraordinary storm named Neptune has given way to fair sky and pink clouds. Leaving like a mangled lizard the body of this huntsman small on the beach. Wet sand inside the clothes and in his hair."

Great Aesculapius knelt—we stood around. With his clairvoyant gaze he demonstrated the corpse: clairvoyant but that always proved to be nothing but immediate inference from natural signs; or not even inference but directly reading it off, for he was there, saying, "But you are *still* doing it! You are doing it right now!"

He said, "This used to be Hippolytus the son of Theseus. Falsely accused; he never felt anything for that woman. He never had such thoughts at all. But *why* did he not?" asked the physician sharply. "If he had thought more of living, he would be still alive."

He turned to us simply, as if he had lost interest in the body. "This is not a profitable question. Let us rather ask:

150

how did he not?" Surprisingly our teacher's face was contorted with resentment. "All right, let me reconstruct the scene. He is standing in her presence provocatively, his head high and laughing in her face, here is the laugh, his pelvis forward, and sometimes he lightly fingers himself without a thought. Phaedra stares at him, but he responds to her gaze not by recognizing it for what it is, but by becoming all the more animated and cocky. His forehead is too immobile. Such is the provocation practiced by young huntsmen who have no thoughts of love, either to suffer it or arouse it. Learn to notice this. What they do not express they exhibit. There is absolutely no one who has nothing to do with love.

"He is standing near her and feels he is looked at, but he never comes any nearer. But she stammers and staggers. Next moment, as if there were no such thing, he leaves without a word to shoot arrows at a stag and thrust his spear into the boar. It is hot with these things that he returns and confounds the daughter of the mother who fucked the Bull in the machine."

When he reconstructed this scene, Aesculapius wept. He often wept, it was a way he had of washing his eyes bright.

"The wrath of Theseus," he used to say, "was the pathetic expedient of a man who has neglected a family obligation he does not care for, and he casts the reproach wherever he can."

We see now how the sea became sullen. In his dejection Hippolytus was crouched on the beach like a scared lizard that changes color. He was turning livid like the open space between the black clouds and the black water. The world had a mouth gaping with fear, and on its brow perplexed wrinkles. The waves were shouting, the air holding its breath. Darkness fell. The lizard too turned blue-black. At last Zephyr let out his shriek of fright and the horses of Neptune have leapt onto the beach.—

Theseus wept: "I am an unhappy man. My father Neptune gave me three wishes and I have squandered them all to my disadvantage. Following Pirithous, I wished myself across the Styx in Hell. I did not rescue Pirithous but I found myself trapped among the dead. I wished to be back in the world and I came home and wished for the death of Hippolytus. And now my son is dead."

He is weeping bitterly for Pirithous and the hunting of the Calydonian boar. "I slew Hippolytus because I was unable to rescue Pirithous." He is in despair and he will do himself an injury. Nevertheless he has relented toward himself, because he foreknows that it is necessary for him to act out such wasted wishes, to go to Hell and back and destroy his most beloved son, in order to be rid, in order to become the lawgiver of Athens.

Theseus and our master sailed together on the *Argo*.

2.

Our teacher Aesculapius, he knew of these things, as he stood beside the jetsam body that had wet sand inside the clothes and in the hair. Briefly he described to us the essentials: the young man thoughtlessly provocative, a servant of the virgin Diana; the Venus-sick daughter of Pasiphae; and

the head of the Hero aching with the crown of immortality
of which, however, he would not foreswear a single jewel.

Our master said: "It is senseless. I deny it. No such thing
occurred. I deny it."

He told us this even as he was carefully undressing the
corpse. He said, "There is no such thing."

We asked, "How is this? Do you deny it because it is senseless? Are we to understand that the past makes no sense?"

"No. The past always makes sense. What has occurred is,
in so far, necessary; how could you live otherwise? But not
this. It is senseless because I deny it."

We insisted: "Then why are you so angry about nothing?"

"I? I am not angry. Don't bother me, you are interrupting
our conversation."

And indeed, he was all at once attending to the body with
those eyes of his and his baby-panting breath as you attend
to a second person, saying "You." He brushed us aside, us and
our questions, as though we were discourteously interrupting
a conversation he was having.

But with whom? Was *that* Hippolytus the huntsman?
That thing could not, it did not, counteract the ground-force
alternately to the left and right and run? That ankle, I
thought, could not vault onto any horse; was that an ankle?

The horse was standing quietly among us, nuzzling at me,
and I laid my arm lovingly and admiringly across her neck,
for she was alive. We were both alive. With her animal flair
she knew better than our teacher what the case was, and she
was looking for a new rider.

"Lead that disgusting animal away," snapped Aesculapius,

clairvoyantly observing us with the back of his head. I blushed with hot shame from head to foot.

My teacher rose and turned and lightly touched my shoulders with his palms, and—how shall I say?—he took my blushing and held it before him in space.

Nevertheless, as when a hungry hawk falls suddenly from the sky and strikes, and the lizard lies mangled, but the fluttering bird has not yet picked up his food to fly away with strong strokes, so that body lay worthless on the sand.

"Hippolytus!" whispered the physician, and our hairs stood on end. He was like a fluttering hawk.

He began, while he worked, to carry on a whispered conversation with the corpse, in a familiar vein. The conversation was one-sided. Some of what we overheard was the dirty humor of the Argonauts; he began to tell over, like an old fool, his hoary anecdote about the women of Lemnos. We were embarrassed to crowd closer to listen, embarrassed for him. We were embarrassed for him and nevertheless our hairs stood on end! (How was that?) Meantime, almost stealthily, he kept applying here and there a subtle pressure of his thumbs and fingers like a shrewd fellow making love to an unresponsive whore.

Our general impression was that he was babbling and carrying on not so much to exert any magical influence on that carrion as to convince himself of his own denial that it was dead. To say it crudely, he was wilfully becoming demented, as I have seen the Bacchae.

He was making love to something that had been not only disgustingly a virgin but was now not even alive. When he began to giggle it was beyond anything.

Once again he read our thoughts, as he could, and he said cuttingly over his shoulder: "What you are doing I don't know. As for me, I'm not playing games. Do you think I would deny the evidence of my senses if the non-existence of the thing were not necessary for me? Do you think I would be exerting an effort if I did not hope for success?"

We wished that the earth would swallow us up.

—Savior Twins! and Phoebus the Destroyer! and Aesculapius father of the Asclepiads! under his hands gentle but firm the ribs were breathing, the flesh flushed with color and stood erect, and Hippolytus opened his eyes.

3.

"*Thief!*"

It was the king of Hell stood there and said, "Thief!"

"*I deny it!*" said our physician. "If he had been dead, how is he now alive?"

As for us, we had fallen to the ground and wrapped our cloaks over our heads. (I peered out.)

Aesculapius was green with fear, like the underside of a leaf. That first sentence he had said manly enough; but now his voice stuck in his throat and it came forth, when it came, from the tomb. Yet he stood confronting Pluto; but his knees were knocking and his teeth were chattering.

The god had not yet fully appeared, and we projected into his space each one his own bad dream.

"I know you," said Aesculapius who saw him clearer, "and I am afraid. I do not run away like a live animal only because of these sons who expect of me otherwise. (In so far, I am making a mistake, but I must.)"

"Now five or six times," said the king of Hell, "you have stolen the dead. You brought back Lycurgus and Capaneus and two or three others. Shall Hell be despoiled altogether by you and yours, for we know you train up others? My brother Neptune destroyed Hippolytus; he came to us—"

Oh! a fine band of brothers! a fine band of brothers! Pluto, Neptune, and Jupiter, and the cannibal their father! A tide of resentment flowed hotly into our cheeks and from that moment on we have ceased to shudder forever.

"*I deny it!*" said Aesculapius our spokesman. "There was no such thing as you say. It did not occur." And to our astonishment and glory he found the words for us and cried out, "*Here* you see him! it is Hippolytus. Sit up, boy."

But Hippolytus was pale and faint, and could not.

"Support him!" said the physician.

Willingly two of us supported the young man to his feet. He grew alive under our hands, though he was moaning with pain. Our eyes were blazing with audacity. Our leader was drunken with defiance. We no longer knew what we were doing, nor cared.

The god, of course, was not taken aback. They are what they are. The question is always how we are to cope with that.

Hippolytus, as he stood there supported by us, was not at his best, he was not wearing any laurel wreath, yet he was a very adequate specimen of a living man.

We were frantic with pride.

"So?" said the king of Hell, "you deny it? You deny also, no doubt, the order of natural consequences! A foolish man, a vicious woman, and a callow boy: henceforth, no doubt, one thing is not supposed to lead to another. So say the sons of Aesculapius! Are *you* the ordainer of the heavens and the earth?"

"No, God forbid," said Aesculapius, "God forbid that I should deny the order of consequences, by which alone we have a world not only to our disaster but to our advantage. But am I to take every senseless error or impulse of lust as a fatality? The natural consequences, as you call them, are often only passing symptoms, warnings for our guidance; and these have been given over to the skill of me and mine!"

He spoke it with breath-taking assurance. One could not resist a bleak smile in the very teeth of the god. Yet, to be truthful, it was all a pack of lies, for we *do* steal the dead, whenever we can, and whatever the circumstances!

4.

Turning away from our conversation with a gesture of dismissal, Pluto lifted his fists to heaven.

The king of Hell was, as he appeared, black and noble like Memnon and bejewelled like a mine where falls a pencil of sunlight, and your fingers, if you interpose them, drip fire.

"Jupiter guardian," he said solemnly, "guardian of the divisions of the world, strike him dead. For he has brought to life Lycurgus and Capaneus and Hippolytus and two or three more. They are lying; they do not make exceptions of cases but they steal whenever they can. Finally, he has taken leave of his wits and denies the evidence of his senses."

It thundered. The prayer was heard.

Even so we were not afraid, for there was in our master's voice a lilting tune of revelry as he said: "Presently! presently! I shall croak as I have heard so many others. I am inspirited now by my dispiritment then. I foresee in a few minutes my ending with a croak. The way is clear to me, I have often observed it, I am simply shuddering with terror. There is no alleviating circumstance. I hurry along and insist on the material fact. As a man is irresponsibly drunk with the awareness of nothing but the case how it is with him—farewell, sailors of the *Argo!*"

Never before had we heard from him two consecutive sentences about himself and himself, not attentive to some second person or demonstrating the nature of the case.

A bolt of lightning struck him and he fell forward.

"I can revive Hippolytus"—these were the last words of Aesculapius— "but me I cannot revive."

No! No! —we sing our joyous anthem —No! No! We deny it! We deny it!

It did not happen. There is no such thing. The past is always necessary, you cannot disregard it. But not this.

If he had been dead, how is he now alive?

Deny it! deny it! it is always a question how far you can deny the evidence of your senses and get away with it. As for us, we have a steady will for it to have been otherwise, as Aesculapius revived Hippolytus.

Afterwards who is right, they or we?

All along the shore the waves are regularly falling as loud

as a conversational voice—it is the noise of drop on drop that thunderously accumulates to be this quiet music—as we lightly carry away our comrade: alas! except for us the line of the Asclepiades would be cut short. On the horizon far where the haze is, the tiny horses of Neptune are playing in the shining. The offshore islands are clear in detail where the lobster-men stop off to fuck the sheep. Their boats are beached.

No! No! we sing our joyful anthem; we deny it! we deny it! If he had been dead, how is he now alive? As for us, we go with a steady will for it to have been otherwise. (Afterwards who is right, they or we?)

As a man is irresponsibly drunk with the awareness of nothing but the case how it is with him—do you think we would be exerting an effort if we did not hope for success?

The day is clear as day and March like the start of spring. Everywhere the sky is spreading further than the earth. The clouds are shapes of vapor in the atmosphere. Sunlight is pouring down from the sun, the heat makes us warm. (That past day was. I recall it as a memory, and I have written it down in words.)

No! No! No! No! We deny it! We deny it! We stumble onward with a steady will for it to have been otherwise. As a man is irresponsibly drunk with nothing but the nature of the case—do you think we should deny the evidence of our senses if the non-existence of the thing were not necessary for us?

Not weeping for myself but my self weeping. My only world weeping myself away. My only world crying herself

159

asleep. Not hurt, not lost, but waste. Not weeping for my-self but my self weeping.

Therefore we deny it, we deny it. It did not happen, there is no such thing. We go right forward with a steady will for many things to have been otherwise.

THE EMPEROR OF CHINA

La Gaieté
—Beethoven,
superscription to Opus 127

1.

What does the Master infer? as he sits in his smallness on
the swiftest of the claws of battling tigers; as he stays in the
middle of the whirlwind and so, the only one of us, is still
in the storm.

—That it's not the case, if we spend our strength for a
free stroke, that there's no strength left for another! There
is not a reservoir of force, but force is welling in the soul. If
we *use up* our strength in love, there will be more strength
for labor and beautiful collaboration. And always we are
ready to the present.

To the present: *Ow!* (I am now speaking not for the
Master but for the Emperor of China who often says Ow!)
The wild ducks flying southward rest in the same swamp as

on their way northward: but the winter is upon us. Master, is not this a round, and for me at least not endless? Therefore the little yellowed man, the Emperor of China, is dreaming of immortality, and he has summoned to his court the Master, the sorcerer, to mix for *him* the potion of vitality. But will our Master come?

Ah, as he lingers at his ease in the eye of the startled, swifter than fright, and therefore the only one of us who is not blind, what does the seer see?

—That there is true invention, in social nature and art. It is not the case that what is done is only the hopeless palliative for an old wound. The games of the children are freely inventing the children, as slowly their red stockings flicker across the yard. Our Master waits smiling in the quick of the grievous wound, revelling in the knowledge that Destiny is Providence.

Is Providence: *Ow!* The Emperor knows it well; who can deny that Destiny has brought us one and all to the present moment? And we are rotating as in a whirlpool down into the black heart of our wound. Yes, the destiny of the Emperor of China and of the court of the Emperor of China is the providence of the sadness of all China. Who can deny it, as we slowly one by one slip to our death?

(But it is said that the *people* of China is immortal.)

The Master of the *Way!*—that we see only fitfully, when the curtain of the world happens to be ripped—what does he know, swimming in a gleaming spray-drop and sinking with it into the shining sea?

—He knows that what is best is easiest and what is easiest is best. Does it not rest and slide in the accumulated rage of

162

the universe, and survive in the next motion of the universe as it trembles open into freedom and the present, not otherwise than the trembling daisy stretches to the tips of its many trembling petals? By the best, the easiest, and the latest moment, our friends will everywhere create small worlds of freedom.

But the ancient court of China turns in its tiresome ritual about its sullen wound. And those of the court most ancient and dignified are soonest sucked downward into black hell. It is these mandarins of the court who have said that the energy of the universe and the soul is conserved: that is, that it dribbles away in use, and if a man uses it for love or achievement, he will not have any left. They say, too, that a man becomes a man by giving up the ways of a child, rather than by growing into the glory of the next moment as it comes. So say these circlers of an old wound.

But our Master lay seventy years aforming in the womb, in safety, and *he* will never become a mere personality like you or me.

They imagine, in the red-lacquer court, that they are hoarding their strength. But watch close and you see that their ritual is made of thousands and thousands of pitiful fights with themselves, so minute that they cannot see them, but we see them in the taut tendons and strained eyes. "We cannot!" they cry, and meantime they are exhausting their power as hard as they can to whirl themselves around and downward into black hell. *Ow!*

The Emperor is bleeding. "That sage," he thinks, "is an immortal person"—the fool, for our Master is not even a person, and we doubt that he is immortal. "Send for him

here, to mix me a potion of vitality, and perhaps I shall not
die the moment after next."

Ay, send for him! beyond the Great Wall of the Empire.
But will our Master come? lying stretched in his vastness as
the circle of the horizon. What is our Master planning, as
his thoughts drift across the blue heaven in clouds that are
changeably seen as animals and junks, as they disperse?

—Silence and the Void. That into the silence and the void
melt the gongs and the ritual, and the Great Wall of China
itself. But from a crevice darts, quick as fire, an apprehensive
salamander.

2. *Travel-Song*

Our Master has decided to answer the summons and go to
Pekin.

As the Small Group, the humanity of our Master, goes up
to Pekin, how shall I call it? what seems to be a small band
of persons: children, parents, and friends, and some of these
already dead, accompanying by their absence; and some not
yet born, who accompany by our hope for them. This original humanity, not an individual and not a nation, but the
social nature of the magician—as it goes among the fresh
grass and reading by night the calligraphy of the Northern
Bear trembling in the moist air—is dancing a travel-song.

Its name is *The Easiest, the Best, the Latest Moment.*

The Way is difficult ease. It is hard to do the easy thing,
as to use the strength one has rather than to labor with the
strength that one has not; to stand out of the way and let

the power of the world crowd to our aid, rather than hinder it with obstacles; to go toward an end without using means that hasten away from the end. These easy things are hard to do. But is the easiest thing to do the hardest thing to do? No, there are many harder things, which we see people in fact busy doing, as we see people persevering with their last strength in a course which they know to be disastrous.

In general, there is an easy thing to do that is easy to do. This is not, to be sure, the easiest (which for us in our ignorance is always hard). But to do easily an easy thing is already a good step toward doing with less difficulty the easiest thing.

And sometimes, blessedly! the easiest thing to do is the easiest thing to do! often in moments of great stress, as we see people do immense and intricate heroic deeds, using the strength of the world that is crowding to their aid. Or habitually, in moments of quiet an artist draws the easiest line. Or revelling in despair, as our dear musician sang so lightly agreeing that he would die.

But always the easiest is the best. It is the Way.

So, demonstrating it by dancing it (for this is the easiest way), the social nature of the Master proceeds up toward Pekin.

Now in the opposite direction is coming a herd of sheep. All are in one impulse fleeing toward their slaughter. Each one of these sheep is alone in its rudimentary mind: it is hardly aware of its fellows, except in a few flashes of searing odor or a random urge of lust. Nevertheless all are bound in one direction and moving as one beast. They might be a herd of fifty or a hundred eighty million.

But the magical band of children, parents, friends, the dead, and the unborn has a certain small number, a certain variety of love and rivalry, of need and mutual aid, as on they trembling dance.

Now they are singing that the Latest is the best, the last motion of nature as it flickers through the present into the next motion after the latest. For who can deny that it is most available, it is present to hand, it is the easiest? It crowds upon us, whether we will or no, through all our senses and in our heartbeat, and even in our muscles taut to ward it off! O what are you warding off? Do you not recognize it? it is the present moment crowding into being to our aid, accompanied by the powers of all the past. A little living force, no bigger than a salamander, darting quick as fire from the crevice. A dragon, this present! lying in its vastness around the horizon, enclosing the world.

Let us watch them, dancing to Pekin. They are going on their legs. For they do not roll heels over ears like wheels, as once I thought to be the motion of Paradise before I considered the nature of Earth. For earth is textured, it is solid and uneven to the touch. By its solidity it offers support in order that its unevennesses may be spanned; so *we* proceed by making spans and bridges across the roughness.

And the music of dancing has four gaits: single-time of hopping and jumping, double-time of walking, triple-time of skipping, and quadruple-time of running. All these are native gaits, as you may tell by observing the locomotion of our children. And our social band goes all these gaits, hopping or jumping, walking, skipping or running to Pekin, and waiting up for the aged.

Accompanied too by some who are already dead and do not go these gaits; for the gayety of our natural band is made up somewhat by the presence of their absence.

3.

Our Master has come to the Great Wall. Let us go back to the Court.

The Great Wall of China is complete! and all China realizes with horror that it is imprisoned.

We in the Court have warded off the natural forces and projected them into bricks and commodities, and encysted them in true formulations; now these stand there glowering hostilely at us.

In the court of the Emperor of China, they sound the gong of alarm. The Emperor is dreaming of not dying; he is dreaming of that immortal emperor who never died because he never lived. (But the *people* of China is immortal.)

The Emperor and the Chinese have been hoarding their strength brick by brick. Building the Great Wall of China, feverishly, slowly, each man alone, brick alongside brick, and ordering the rows into a wall, and extending the wall along the survey lines. So one hoards one's strength by deliberate calculation and builds the Great Wall of China.

So an author orders the letters into a neat word. First he has projected the threat of life into a thing, and he denotes the thing in a neat word. Next he sets word next to word in lines, he rules line under line to make up a page. He has now encysted life in true formulations. He arranges these pages in such a sequence . . . This is called warding off the natural forces! protecting himself from joy! hoarding his strength! building the Great Wall of China.

But the Great Wall of China is complete and all China realizes with horror that it is imprisoned. The natural things lie there, glaring hostilely.

Suddenly one is sensible that the whirlpool is turning; and we see how already those nearest the center are being sucked downward into black death. Good-bye to them! one by one.

In the Court of the Emperor of China they sound the gong. The Emperor of China is dreaming of not dying: he is dreaming of that immortal emperor who never died because he never lived.

See *here!* comes colored, motherly of carriage, and floating a foot above the water, the junk of our silent Master—on the escallops of the whirl and spray. The sails are colored with the feelings Carefree, Omniregardant; her flag is Super-Abounding and her pennons Toothless Smiles. Patience Firmness Duty: these are her carriage, the same as the endurance of the world: who rests in it upborne more lightly than a babe.

She floats by Non-Attachment. She comes by the Disclosure of the Next Moment.

She pauses in mid-air in the maw of the whirlpool. From the slippery wall of water is thrust a forearm with a despairing clutch, but cannot touch her.

Nevertheless our Master makes himself heavy and slowly sinks into the bite of pain.

4.

La Gaya Scienza
—Nietzsche

While the wizard sinks, he swallows the space about and recreates a void.

While the diabolical magician brews the poison potion for the Emperor, he observes silence.

Silence: but the Silence! For there is a kind of lesser silence, when one does not talk or sing, as when a person is alone. Such a silence is not even refreshing, for one carries on silent wrangles and mutters his composition. Deeper than this there is a better silence that, if one observes it, is indeed refreshing, yet it is not the Silence: this is when a person listens and does not think of answering, as when we listen to frogs in the marsh and look at everything attentively. This silence is recreative, and finally we break it with a melody from nowhere. A good sign, but still it is not the Silence.

For always we are still forming concepts and judgments and inwardly saying: "It is the croaking frog—" "The interval is a minor third—" "See the dark line of the hills." This inward speech, that seems to be only listening and taking in the scene, is betrayed by our small gestures, the motions of swallowing, of darting eyes, as we say to ourselves, "this" and "next?"

How to be silent? and not always forming concepts and judgments? As for me, I am *expert* in formulations; these I can always make and say, "there it is!" "that is what it is!"

"it is only that, don't fear!" "Next?" There is no doubt of it, that I talk and think too much, and write too much. Yet let me speak no evil of the creator spirit, listening to whom, over my shoulder, and taking in the scene, I joyfully make my true formulations. But it is *not* meant that I should use them to ward off the world.

The Silence of the magician is before he has learned to speak, as we speak; before he is formed a personality, as we are personalities.

The images float across his sky like clouds. They split with fire and there is a crack of thunder. It is raining. For in the Silence, our Master, who lay seventy years in the womb, is playing with the milk, the drool, the turds, the piss, the blood, and the semen.

In the void, in the quick of the wound, where the wizard has swallowed up the space, he is dancing the Creation of the Things Before They Have a Name.

—That the drool and the milk and so forth are the Rivers of Paradise.

That when he masturbates he opens high and wide the dome of Heaven.

That sinking and losing the weight of his body, he divides into territories at his bony joints, and these are the six Continents and their mountain ranges.

That from turds he fashions out the elephants and the bears.

That when he f.s, the electric friction makes the sky blue. The thick lightning.

170

From the seed the magician is born again, that lay seventy years in the womb. The Master of *La Gaya Scienza!*

(As for me, natural things are no longer so hostilely glowering.)

In the Silence, in the Void, things fall of their weight. They drop lightly into place. They tremble open to the most space to the present flowers of May. The wild ducks are flying northward. The moments are flying thick and fast, but they are not flying by, they are not flying by. The Master of *La Gaya Scienza* is dancing us the things that do not yet have a name. Thick and fast the moments are not flying by.

Now, in the hole of the vortex, in the clenched jaws of death, the hellish wizard is spinning like a dervish and his skirts fly out. He has made his excrements into missiles and is destroying those who love him. He sucks their breasts and will not let loose with his teeth. They are drowned in the searing piss, beaten by his virile club, and jumped on up and down. All things are flying from him as he spins: he spins alone: his skirts fly out. Can we ever restore to place those things flung far from their center? Too late! Our future has been swallowed up by a wizard.

We were omnipotent when we destroyed it; but now when we would restore it, we are not omnipotent. *Never* can we make restitution. *This* is the grievous wound by which we are bleeding to death.

5.

Wifely, high: like the moon rescued from the slime after a fortnight we did not see her and all at once shining at a bound in the top of heaven, such are the full sleeves that offer to the Emperor the cup of vitality. The beverage that is brewed of animal spirits, that is fermented for the duration of the world, and distilled into presentness. The revolution that is frothing at the brim never ceases. Drinking, our natural band will go the wandering way that does not err.

But the Emperor of China sips this poison and straightway he falls down in death agony, croaking.

For the Emperor of China summoned the Master of the Way and bade him brew for him the elixir of immortality; but drinking it, he is poisoned and falls down in his death agony. Is this the fault of the elixir?—The Master is impassive.

The Emperor of China cries out, croaking: "*Ow! I know* that destiny is providence; my brain is seared with it, as a tongue of fire licks from the window and envelops the house. Hurrying on, I have come back again and again to my wound, and who can deny that the past is crowding into this present moment and the next and last? Am I supposed therefore, in the jaws of death, to sing out joyfully, 'Ah! providential!' *Ow!* Yet indeed, the natural things are no longer glaring at me so hostilely. They are impassive. Even the Great Wall of China is only a broken wall. What drink is this that you have poisoned me with? The revolution frothing at the brim does not cease. Ow! I know! Is it not the same

172

thing to say Ow! and I know? Who is this impassive dragon lying around the circle of the horizon with his tail in his mouth? It means that my time is complete. I am the immortal emperor, who never died because he never lived. Tell me, is it *thus* that the people of China will be immortal?"

He is dead. What? are they not going to proclaim another?

The Master says: "Why didn't he drink of it a second time?"

6.

The Master says, "Why didn't he drink of it a second time?"

He says: "Is not every natural force violent? Violent clashes with violent, and there emerges, trembling, what was not known before. This is called Brotherly Conflict and Invention.

"When a man is in prison himself, must not nature seem to be the destruction of the world?

"When a man is imprisoned, this is called Dreaming of Immortality.

"But 'the hounded hare takes pleasure in his leaps, in his dodges, in his speedy course.' "

The mandarins of China—looking each man with wide eyes at his startled friend—say to one another: "*Therefore* let us set free the people of China.

"It is said that the people of China is immortal. Perhaps they can teach us to be immortal. Or at least! at least that we, in our yellowed age, may have a little comfort in watching the inventive games of the children of the people of China, as slowly their red stockings flicker across the yard.

"That we may rest from building the Great Wall of China, no longer hoarding our strength and making true formulations.

"In order that the natural things may not glower at us so hostilely.

"To cease to turn about our grievous wound.

"To dance into the present with the force of the endurance of the world."

I. *A Statue of Strength and Weakness*

1.

This allegorical sculpture consists of two figures, Strength and Weakness, represented by a man and a woman. Strength is constraining her on her back, mostly by his mass and weight rather than his power, his knee in her belly, his legs pinning her knees; and his two hands are grasping her wrists, keeping her arms wide and helpless. On the face of Strength is a look of intense perplexity.

The meaning of his perplexity is that Strength does not want to exert force on Weakness, yet she is intent on hurting him, wants to hit him. On his left shoulder and the right side of his back, he is marked with bleeding scratches that she inflicted before he pinned her.

Being powerful, Strength wants not to force but to rule.

But this puts him in difficulty when his power is challenged by the violence of Weakness. The difficulty is expressed by the perplexity on his face, but even more tellingly by the strain of his muscles far beyond what is needed to hold her down, as if he hoped to subdue her merely by forced *inaction*, while at the same time not transmitting his hurtful power to her but constraining it within himself. The real struggle is the knot of his own muscles. If the stone could speak, he would be saying, "Do you give up?"—when she will not give up.

But Weakness, on the contrary, wants to strike and be struck just in order to have her own nature be proved; what she wants is not to be ruled but to be defeated. Therefore on her face is a look of exultant wilfulness and guile; she is waiting her chance. So it is Strength who bears the marks of wounds and effort, whereas Weakness is happy and untouched. This is a triumph of the artist who thereby, in expressing her nature, can avoid portraying any ugliness of deficiency.

So these two remain fixed, by his perplexity and her wilfulness; and it is this static moment that the sculptor has seized on for his composition.

2.

But it is not only in this moment of spurious external struggle that Strength is characterized by the conflict among his own powers. The artist has seized on the present struggle to show obvious signs of this interior conflict, a knot of muscles, a frown. But by these he calls attention to other features of the figure of Strength that are *not* involved in the unequal external struggle but express the *habitual* constraint that characterizes him. Thus, the habit-formed lines of his face express the day to day perplexity of withholding his full powers in order not to do damage in the world as it is. The modeling of his ankles and toes has a nervous alertness whose meaning is deep just because in the present struggle he has no need of it, for it is clear that by the weight of his knee and shoulders alone, resting in her belly and pinning her arms, he is easily able to hold her down. By these details we are shown the Strength of all his life, as it acts in this particular conflict but abides in him in every case.

Seen so, his posture is almost that of a dancer rather than a wrestler. There is something fastidious and almost effeminate, in the way he doles out his force in accordance with the just measure of an idea rather than the vigor of an instinct. Except that he seems to be saying, "It's not yet time!" to loose his forces. And we are overwhelmed by the pathos of waste, for when will it ever be the time?

What is here presented to us, we realize in a flash, is an effigy of Fear! Certainly not fear of something in front, but self-fear. What *crime* is it he sees inside him, that keeps him from striking, perhaps from striking *again*? Did he once strike?

So it is not far-fetched that helpless Weakness will not give up now. For she is in danger. And this gives a *dark* sense to that look of baffled perplexity on the face of Strength.

And we see, now, why the artist has shown us the woman untouched. In this allegorical art where the outward shows the inward, she is not wounded nor contorted by guilt. Her

177

wilfulness is innocence. Her hair is widespread on the ground; her lips and eyes are wide; there is here nothing guarded. She is willing to scatter her resources, even to blows given and received. She is screaming, in stone.

In such a moment, before the perpetration of a crime, the sculptor has fixed these two forever.

3.

It is odd. The stone figures seem to be in motion!

Is not Strength in the very act of bringing down his great head and shoulders in a kiss? and she of relaxing to this kiss? His hands, we see, are *slipping* from her wrists to cover her hands palm to palm; and his knee is sliding to rest touching her knee. This is why he is withholding his weight: it is with the considerateness of a lover, for it is not yet time to lie full weight. It will be time when their excitement is intense enough to transmute force and pain into pleasure. What we took to be a fastidiousness in his posture is nothing but the indefiniteness of beginning to change position. The perplexity on his face is his passing from one thought to another; one would say that he has just noticed that she is no longer resisting.

The artist has seized on a kind of *lapse* between strong contraries in order to get the static moment for sculpture, and thereby he seems to have dissolved the fixity of sculpture into motion; for the eye cannot rest in this presented moment.

It is a natural transition. For it is not with impunity that, body to body, they have paralyzed their own strongest purposes. They are unprepared for the feeling that wells up.

Only love can dissolve the thunderous block of place in which Strength has imprisoned himself. Only gentle Violence can assuage the crime to which he is paralyzed to commit himself.

The sculptor has chosen the moment when the lovers are confused, lost. Yet—not like the melting loves of Rodin—they are quite disengaged from the formless rock.

Now notice how the artist has given to Strength, and to the breasts of the woman, the beginning of erection. In this there is nothing far-fetched; it would often occur in persons wrestling.

II. *A Page of Sketches of Fights*

Hot Fighters

These two fighters have one mind, to cut each other down. They are going about it hot, doing as much immediate damage as possible, neither one defending himself. Yet they do not much feel their hurt because each is thinking only of destroying the other. Hurt is a blast blowing up the fire. Stung, they hit harder.

They do not frustrate each other. It is even conceivable that both could succeed: for instance, if it is a boxing match, the one might knock out the other and be standing over him with glassy eyes, but when the referee counts four, he himself falls down unconscious.

Each is not much aware of his own body, nor that his legs are braced against the ground. The blows he throws are attracted by, created by, the face to be demolished, and he does not hear his hissing breaths nor feel how his punches have bounded up from the center of the earth. But the impact is glowing loud with joy.

Neither has the aim to inflict damage, but simply to destroy. So naturally they inflict a lot of hurt and damage until, according to their unequal power and skill and luck, one of them is no longer able to carry on his single-minded aim. He is surprised when he is no longer busy cutting the other down. He was not counting on any other possibility. His damaged body has suddenly become a huge thing. And the object before him is fading away, out of reach. A fist looms and hits him—this time he is immensely aware of its slow coming—and he falls.

Looming over him, the face of the victor only momentarily flashes the look of achievement, for it is at once crossed by trying to remember his ulterior purpose in the fight. So the one lies with a look of surprise in his anguish, and the other in his success has a wandering mind.

A *Cold Fighter*

This time, with the fighter single-minded to destroy is matched a man who is prudently defending himself against being hurt, biding his time till he can coldly smash and cut his opponent down. This man is not single-minded for he is afraid of hurt and death, but he controls his fear by will.

Soon the anger in the fight is streaked with hatred. Perhaps, just as he defends his body with his guard, the cold and deliberate fighter is warding off feeling hurt by taking relish in smashing the other towards his finish. He wants to *damage* him, it is part of his plan. And he is conscious of throwing every blow.

But suppose that for a moment (or for good) he himself is badly hurt and loses control of the fight, while the other still keeps coming single-mindedly to get him. He is in confusion and may be gripped by panicky fear, not knowing what to do and unable to rally spontaneously. For, centered in himself, he has *not* simply been conveying his punches coming up from the center of the earth through his heels across his back to their impact, and now he is out of touch. He crouches as small as he can behind his guard, while the aggressor rains blows on that not impregnable fortress.

But communing with himself behind his guard, he recovers control, he raises his head, and he resumes with a more steely will, like an ax. And finally he has put together enough damaging blows to cut his opponent down, like a tree. Then he stands over him, breathing heavily, safe, clenching and unclenching his fists, beginning to mutter—till at last his passion rises to the surface and he is shaking with rage.

Heads of Victors

A boy who has fought single-mindedly only to destroy his opponent, and then afterwards his wandering mind finally realizes that he has won: he is grinning and waving his hands in rapturous appreciation of himself, and shouting, "Ma! I won! I won!"

Another boy who fought single-mindedly, but fighting is the only thing in the world that he does honorably and naively, so afterwards his face at once narrows again to the settled suspicious leer of a conceited gutter rat.

Another boy, a deliberate and skillful killer who has maintained all through the fight an impassive countenance; but now he is swept by uncontrollable fear and you can hear the loud clicking of his teeth.

A Coward

A coward, whose blind terror of hurt or death—or simply of the fact that the other is angry with him—has paralyzed his arms so that he can neither strike a blow nor even lift his guard to protect himself. The other slugs him.

His only recourse is to fall down and be passive, screaming in pain even before he is hurt. But this is not a defense, for the other simply mauls and kicks him like a sack. This beating is not cruel so long as the aim is single-minded to destroy him rather than to hurt or damage him. It is ugly when, as a worthless hoodlum might beat a cowardly homosexual, he is vindictively punishing him and taking satisfaction in that; or both are taking satisfaction in that.

But the radical evil in cowardice is that the coward, unable to stand up for himself, has nevertheless adventured into this situation where he has to fight. Doing so, he has not respected, he has violated, his own animal terror, his timorous nature. A man like that should be circumspect.

But it happens that just when he is being beaten up, he may suddenly no longer be paralyzed. In a flash he single-mindedly accepts his terror and, jumping up by surprise, he takes to his heels. He is likely to get away, for his fright is stronger than the killer's will.

Then the tables are turned. The coward is a coward no longer, but simply a weaker but swifter man. He taunts and jeers at his enemy from a safe distance and makes him look like a fool.

A Man Forced Into a Fight

Yet it is a melancholy but common thing in the world (and makes for a melancholy world) that while the one fighter is for some reason single-mindedly bent on destroying a man, that man does not want this fight; he does not believe in it, he does not think that it is worth the hurt and damage involved. He has been forced into it, and it happens that he cannot quit the field.

Even though he guards himself skillfully, he continues to be hurt and damaged. He fights poorly because he does not mean it, to destroy or even hurt the aggressor, but he wants to establish some different relation with him which is incompatible with fighting with him, but which the other will not allow him to establish.

Hurt, he is not stung but made sick. Naturally, doing something that seems to him senseless, he is awkward. It is evident that he is pulling his punches, so that he looks disdainful, too proud to fight or too superior to fight; indeed, he *is* disdainful; except that he is bewildered what to do and he is wincing because he is badly hurt. But even worse, if he happens for a moment to be stung and comes back fighting strong, he is at once paralyzed by prudence, knowing that any damage he now inflicts he will later have to remedy.

So even a strong, wise, brave, and benevolent man is often cut to pieces in this world by the passionate intensity of weakness and ignorance. Somehow he cannot draw on the strength he has. (How then does he "have" it?)

He is felled and on his face are hurt feelings at having been misunderstood. The glee on the face of the victor standing over him fades to its usual spiteful stupidity.

Arjuna

Is the just man, then, powerless? No, for here finally is a fight—if it can be called so—where though the one fighter is single-mindedly in error bent on destroying a superior man, the superior man is going about his duty and is *incidentally* cutting him down like an executioner. Like an executioner, continually drawing on the power that is in patience, wisdom, compassion, and the joy of life.

This hero is no warrior. He is fastidiously afraid of being hurt, for he has an affectionate love for his body. But he draws courage, as Socrates said, from his idea. The superior man is not fighting in *this* fight (perhaps in some different fight in which he is in agony at midnight, for he is not too proud to fight), nevertheless his fist is a hammer from which the other reels back stunned. And though the inferior man rallies viciously, the right is like an impersonal sledgehammer and fells him.

It was not the hero's wish to degrade his opponent who was so fanatically throwing away his life in despair, unable to prevail against the future of the nature of things; but inevitably the poor wretch takes his defeat as an insult and expires purple with rage, as ignorant in death as he was in life.

The victor is Arjuna, to whom evil does not cling as water does not cling to the shining lotus. He is standing in his chariot with Krishna the charioteer, and they sound their whelks named Fivefold and God-Given.

Heads of Beaten Men

The head of a man who has fought single-mindedly in error, and still in death he imagines that he was worsted by a trick. There is unbelief in his glazed eyes.

The head of another man with closed eyes, smiling, enlightened in death by the precious knowledge that he no longer has to try.

THE COMPLAINT OF RICHARD SAVAGE

—*"charioted by Bacchus and his pards"*

1.

"Don't give it a 2nd thought," said I. "After a certain number of drinks you begin to have the thinks even *before* the one you're thinking. Let's call that certain number of drinks *n*. The n + 1 drink gives you the T — 1 think. The n + 7 drink gives you the T — 7 think."

I was beginning to be animated and friendly, but the feeling was already passing over into fright. The hand I was reaching out to touch her ass was freezing and was about to push her away. Next moment I made an angry fist; I jammed it into my pocket in order not to see it crooked. Sometimes, especially if I fell into a rage, my hand was *my* hand; other times I did not recognize it, it was none of mine.

Nobody knew me at this place (where I did not know myself). So long as I remained anonymous, I did not need to tell my lamentable story. As for me, I am ready to take up with anybody that will—I don't ask who *they* are. I suppose I have no standards; from whom should I have gotten standards? The question is how, living this way, I haven't come fatally to grief? The answer is simple.

The answer is simple! Those who are willing to befriend me are only the noblest and the best. I ask for what nobody can give, and I am surly (you will find) when I am frustrated. I offer to give what nobody can safely take, and I am stubborn and persistent in dealing it out. Whoever can put up with me is doomed to greatness! Am I a flatterer? Yes. I flatter you by assuming that the impossible is still possible. Naturally the ordinary person becomes anxious. . . .

Now she was looking in fright at the fingers twitching in space between us; she imagined I was going to pick her pocket. I regarded the hand curiously: did it intend to steal? and what did it intend to steal? My embarrassment gave way to anger and I angrily anticipated her and exclaimed: "You sit there so offish, very well contained in your skin. My compliments—" The thought that I remembered at the n + 7 drink was this: that our lives are the give-and-take of an organism and its environment; and around this thought there played a promissory glory; it seemed to me to be a means of persuasion. "My compliments to you and your touchable skin," I said; "but the case is that no such thing *exists* as an animal in its own skin. If it weren't for the gravity and the ground holding you up, you couldn't be sitting there on your ass. It's the weight of the atmosphere all the way from the moon that's shoving that drink down your throat. May I buy you another? allow me. Hey, cap—"

But as happens always, the force of my persuasion at once worked on myself and plunged me into deep gloom before ever I could reach a conclusion advantageous to us both. (Whatever the truth is, it makes me sad. It is truth that makes me sad.) I felt desolate. But *she* wasn't moved at all.

I remember that I was breathing deeply, invaded by the air and mixing in the air; then suddenly I rose in power, and *what were all these things to me?* (T — 8)

2.

Next thing I remember: there was a small dead end square. The cars and trucks were roaring past its mouth, but no engines came into that cloister except a small green roadster parked under a quarter inch of dust. Here the boys and girls of 8 to 12 were playing a square ball-game and screaming and shrieking, or sometimes calling out to one another the encouraging words: "No matter how closely you contrive your folly roaring to hell, there are dead ends of quiet around the periphery. And time has always its fringe of present actuality, as it goes over the edge."

For these children were making up the actuality as they went along. In their style, playing our funny quick New York ball-game: neat throws with English bounces and sharp smashes aimed at a precise opening between. Yet next moment the ball was swallowed by the fielder without a trace. The hitter was off in a flash—in an instant stopped; and the nonchalance fell on his shoulders like a cape.

I staggered by here drunk, finding it hard to keep in touch with the present actuality. If I broke into panic flight to escape, I was stopped short by the riptide of wheels across my toes. If then, willingly enough, I swayed from side to side in serene contemplation of such a sea of billows surging around my knees, I fell head foremost into a field of broken stones. Some one kept changing the environment. It was no advantage at all toward my happiness to initiate the locomotions of desire, for some one kept changing the environment.

But I turned to confront my huge slumber overwhelming towards me, and with a sigh of pleasure I staggered and fell into the dead end safe haven. I was on the children's ball field and the last thing I heard as I rolled on my side and slept was their groans. "Jesus, he's on the field!"

In this way I became 3rd base. They made up ground rules relating to me, and my left foot was 3rd base. Unlike me, those children were adept at the actuality. Surely they pierced the meaning of the couplet of Jenye:

> "As I cross the river
> it is the bridge that is flowing under my feet."

As for me, to be 3rd base was to get more than one wild kick when the runner failed to cut the corner in his desperate dash for home. Home!

Such kicks make no difference to me! For still beyond the curtain of the present, and again the present, and again the present, there exists the deviating Way.

> "Great Tao is a ship adrift!"

(Indeed it is by a misunderstanding that the thousands line the shore and wave their flags when I come into port. For it was not I that was doing the steering.)

I courteously waited until the last inning to awake. A pair of blue jeans was standing with his foot pressed against my outcast foot. I sat up. I saw that the enclosure of red brick was about 36 feet square. The sun of May late afternoon was blazing in the windows of the eastern side, but I could not interpret the signals. The girls and boys came and formed a semi-circle in front of me, to urge me to get the hell out of the way.

But *their* way was not necessarily the Way. "Oof, what a dream!" I said, following my own bent not theirs. I passed my hand across my face and found reality a little clearer on the other side.

"Whadje dream, mister?" asked the kid who had been standing on 3rd base and was therefore more intimate with me than the others.

"I dreamt that a leopard was chasing me and he caught me and ate me up."

"Jeez! what did *you* do?"

"I tasted good."

"Oh, that was Christian of you!"

It was a dream of poverty and need, such as we might well dream whose mothers often told us not to waste anything. (My own mother, to be sure, set me a more exacting task.) And yet there is no need; the nature of things, the nature, is momently pouring forth its bounty; but we can hardly believe it. Suspicious, we do not take it; and grudging, we do not give it out.

3.

When I stood up, they drew back, by a law of the organ-
ism/environment field that I have frequently observed. (I
have observed nothing else.) While I lay there, a base, I was
a domesticated nightmare, like the stone head from Easter
Island that they show on the top floor of the Museum of
Natural History. But when I rose to my feet I was the terrible
Bacchus, looming unpredictably in the circumscribed space.

It was they, not I, who were trapped in the actuality. At
that moment I could by persuasion or violence—and these
are the same, for one cannot help but hypnotically identify
oneself with superior force—I could have led them after me
in a train and over the edge, as the Pied Piper opened the
hole in the mountainside.

My head was swimming and my senses were dark. It did
not seem to me questionable to wreak vengeance on the children for my indignities. But I dismissed this thought for
another time (when it would return in less convenient circumstances).

Instead I turned my wrath against myself and so began my
usual complaint, reverting, as I recovered my wits, to the
thought T — 7. "As I stand in front of you girls and boys,"
I began.

When it was evident that I was after all only a loquacious
drunkard, the young ones took courage and listened to me
awhile with apprehensive smiles of contempt. One forward
girl waved her hands in the air and conducted me like an
orchestra.

"As I stand here," I said, "my weight goes right down to the center o' the earth. I don't support myself. Did you ever think o' that? But if they keep taking away my environment, how can I stand?"

At this, I swayed more than a little and staggered, but I didn't fall flat on my face. "That's just a slip!" I said. "The earth is there good enough, solid rock, right down to the middle." I stamped my foot and proved it.

Slowly I shook my head from side to side. I was a boxer badly hurt. This lasted half a minute that I said nothing, for I was staggered by the force of the truth that struck me.

"What's the matter, mister, you going to be sick?" said the forward girl, and stopped conducting.

"It's only the human beings who don't know how to give and take," I said. "You kids don't realize it yet, but you'll learn." The next moment I was moved to song, and now I really began to sing, in a strong baritone,

> "Aaaall of me!
> Why not take aaall of me?—"

But now that I was really singing, the girl was no longer conducting, and nobody joined in the song that had been popular before their time. I had frightened them when I stamped on the ground with my hoof, and then lapsed into a silence awful in my own ears. The impact of my stamping in fact did go right down to the center, and it was as if they were waiting for the re-echoing earthquake.

My head was clear. I saw them all, the scene of rose, black, and white, like a photograph of long ago.

My more intimate friend was regarding me judiciously.

"You know, mister," he said, "what you say is all a lot o' bullshit."

"What's wrong with bullshit!" I roared, for I cannot brook contradiction. "If you play with a bull, naturally! What else can you expect!"

There was something menacing in my aspect, for they cried out in fright and fled from the mouth of the cul-de-sac into the heedless traffic.

This made me hopping mad. It was again, *in parvo*, just what I was griping about in the big things. But there was no little and no big, it was the identical law of the organism/environment field. Namely, as soon as the going gets rough, *they* give up the actuality, my actuality, the one and only actuality that I have; and around me there spreads a vacuum.

Since I was hopping in any case, on my left foot, I took off my right shoe and threw it in a rage at the impassive wall. I was dancing about in choliambs, "lame iambics," putting my other foot down on every fifth beat, ∪′ ∪′ ∪′ ∪′′∪.

4.

After a while I turned to go.

"Here, you'll need this," said the boy, appearing from the dusty green roadster and handing me my shoe.

"I see you didn't run away with the others," I said.

"Naw, I didn't. Are you still a little drunk?" he said curiously, for I was trying to put the one shoe on the other one. It was as if he asked, "Do you still have a little environment, or are you finally only an animal contained in your skin?"

I saw that he intended to pan-handle me. I was pleased with the acumen with which he sized me up for an easy mark who still had a couple of dollars. He had orange hair—gray eyes—a faded sweater: it was impossible to take him in as a single whole, the colors fled apart. His style was brisk, but his voice came from the realm where there is no direction because there is no likelihood.

He was reviewing in his mind which of many unattainable things he would grant himself.

"Gimme—Mister," he began, "could you gimme—could you contribute half a buck to the Floyd Lewis Air-Rifle Fund? Half a buck and then we finish up the drive, we're over the top! I'd make you out a raffle-ticket, but between you and I they're phoney, and anyhow I left 'em home. But I gotta get that rifle, 'cause this way—just like you said—I'm left out o' everything an' I'm ashamed an' disgraced in front o' all my contemporaries. But if you gimme the dough," he went on breathlessly, "God bless you. I'll pray to Mary muvver of God to bless you an' all the saints an' St. Cecily because you sing and dance."

"Yes," I said.

"*Will* ye?" he cried, astonished but not unbelieving.

The tears had started into my eyes when I said "Yes," and now they were rolling down my cheeks.

"Whaddye cryin' about?" said Floyd. "You don't need to feel sorry on *my* account. I don't need the f. gun that bad," he said angrily. "Whaddye take me for! a beggar?" He was beginning to beat about for a means of nullifying my help, "All the same I could use that air-rifle," he said, beginning to hop.

"What could you use it for?"

"To shoot out the lamps, o' course."

I forced the coin into his hand, and the tears rolled down my face.

"Jeez, keep your lousy money!" he shouted, beside himself. "D'ye think I takes money from a drunk that's so stingy he's cryin' when he gives it away?"

"Listen, peanut," I said, "I'm not crying because *you* need anything, I assure you. People don't cry for other people, they cry for themselves, you'll find that out when you get older. I'm crying because you happen to need something and ask for it and *I* happen to be able to give it to you. That's why I'm crying."

"F' Crissake, that's a hell of a reason. You're drunk." He saw the coin in his hand and he flung it on the ground. " 'Ts no good to me. There ain't no Floyd Lewis Air-Rifle Fund, an' there ain't no raffle-tickets even if they're phoney."

Naturally we were not, he and I, among those who ask for what we need and could possibly get. (But it is not for *this* reason that we don't get it.)

"O Mary, whaddye *bawlin'* for?" he cried in consternation.

I seized him grimly by the scruff of the neck and he cried out in pain. "How much is the air-rifle?" I asked sternly.

"There ain't no air-rifle, either," he whimpered.

I tightened my grip on his neck. "*Where* is the store?" I said. I was not crying now; my tears had dried up in hot wrath, which is the nearest I ever come to compassion. Damn him! He *got* his air-rifle in spite of himself screaming with fright and lust.

5.

I understand that I am greedy; no doubt of it, I want more than is good for me or than I can digest. Having been starved, afraid of starving—I desperately clutch at the present—and drive it away. I can't help it: when I walk the streets and see the possibilities of joy, that are in fact impossibilities, I am *not* reconciled to the niggardliness of my fortune. I understand that I am niggardly to myself, too. I often prevent myself from taking what is reasonably offered, I am disappointed even beforehand (the while I clutch at something else and try to squeeze water from a stone). All right then, but why don't they *help* me, and more *insistently* make me their reasonable offer? "A person like you, disappointed beforehand, is hard to help." What a thing for her to say! to be offering help and say that help is being offered, when in fact she does not help *me*, in the way that *I* can be helped? What kind of help is that, that I can circumvent?

My name is Richard Savage. I am the son of that unnatural mother who cast me off to begin with and has, inexplicably vindictive, hounded me ever since. The story is by now well known, how she deprived me, who had nothing, of even that which I had, opportunity. Everybody knows it; there is no use for me to repeat my complaint, what I remember and what I fail to remember; but I find myself complaining it nevertheless. She cast me off, I say, as I—as I cast off that shoe—I confess I am beside myself. Hopping—

Oh forget my mother! no matter about my mother! For I see that all of us, not only I, are treated like stepchildren of nature. Nobody gets what he needs. And if you make the mistake of asking directly for what you need, ha, you'll find that *you're* the one that's moved, nobody else, and you'll wish you hadn't mentioned it because the truth is too hard to take. *My* life-story is no worse than the rest, only more obvious, more spectacular, so nobody can deny the truth. (Yet surely there is a misunderstanding, for indeed we are not the stepchildren of nature but her children and rightful heirs.)

Inevitably I have an unresponsive wife. Being as I am, what other wife would I cleave to? I give her my hand, my want— oh, she is unmoved by this. She does not push me away, but she lies there in sullen silence. And what is the result of banging myself against a flank that does not respond? Instead of being jovially proud of my powers—such as they are! such as they are!—I am made to feel inferior. Inferior? to whom? for what? You may well ask.

And so I burst into tears when I say the word "Yes." Crying not because the urchin asked me for something he could not get; but on the contrary, that he asked for something that, as it happened, he *could* get. For an instant my mother had relented. Relented! And all at once I caught a glimpse of lost paradise and the tears started into my eyes. But it is paradise lost—I am forty years old—crying for myself.

Bawling because it was I—notice! please! look at me!—it was I who was graciously extending the bounty of nature. Oh, this is a role I play with grace, with delicacy, to the manor born! I play it like a baboon. The boy was screaming when I gave him a gift.

Naturally this is all spite. I understand this. Frustrated, I complain in order to make you unhappy too. But what's

wrong with spite? It is the last resource of us powerless who
cannot fight back any more, but we can vent our spite. Of
course spite doesn't accomplish anything, but it is a way we
have of remaining alive, of not simply succumbing. You who
are not spiteful in this world have long ago given up in
despair; I say it spitefully.

6.

> When I was trapped, tired and bored,
> I sent my shadowself abroad:
> > went down the street and boldly had
> > the simple joy I was afraid
>
> to take—that even easily
> the world might have given me.
> > And he returned and was glad
> > and stood beside where I sat sad.
>
> "Why do you come back?" I said
> "and not abandon me for dead
> > with this body that I cannot use?"
> > But so it was, and so it is.

7.

I keep telling my story for spite in order to watch your
faces fall and take the joy out of your lives.
But you aren't even suckers for it and you stubbornly won't

listen to me—you make as if I didn't exist—and so this too has become part of my story.

Maybe it's finally the most essential part: that you won't even listen to me. Then the question is this: if you'd listen and I had *this* satisfaction, would I let up on the rest of my vindictiveness—granted my vindictiveness is justified, you'd have to grant me that—let up and agree to do a stroke of useful work to add to the general welfare? But there is no way of testing this question either.

Why you should listen to me when I mean only to cause you pain, is beyond me.

Because I will it, and you won't. If you all weren't so damned stubborn, I wouldn't persist. Agh, so much for that!—

"So much for that! Now for these Irish wars," as Dick the Second said.

8.

My shadowself came back and found me at McHale's Tavern, which is in a way my other home, on Eighth Avenue at 26th Street. Here there were as always the three primordial elements of gayety: music, bright lights, and liquor.

Music! think of it a moment: how the skillful corporation of the musicians, trained one generation to another from the remotest antiquity, are still making for us jaunty music on savage instruments, and Persian instruments, and Italian instruments;

and Lights! think how these illuminations, boxes of fire in

the transparency, have been continually elaborated by the generations of Prometheus to brighten our spirits and let us see;

and how the brewers, experienced, experimenting always new fruits and ferments, coctions and distillations, fix in this bottle the happy result sometimes achieved by chance;

to think that these age-old quintessences of human wit should have combined to no more merry hour than this, at this dismal McHale's Tavern! The identical elements of excitement! and this is the result! How is it possible? how did it come to pass? There was from the beginning, surely, a crack in our golden goblet, and the joy ran out.

"All right! I *have* thought of it!" said I to myself. "And supposing it is just as you say, what must I conclude?"

"What do you mean?" I said. "You must conclude that it is all very discouraging."

"Good. I grant you that it is discouraging. What then?"

"What then? What do you mean, What then?"

"I mean, you demonstrate that we are in a dreadful way, and then what follows?"

I fell silent. There was a pause. In this pause I was aware of how it was there, of the tinkling notes and the sparkling little pictures in the glasses, the apple-jack in my mouth, and so forth and so forth.

"Don't you see," I said gently, "you cannot conclude where you do, for you must *still* confront the present actuality passing over into the next."

I said it gently, changing my tone toward myself. For ordinarily we intellectuals are too hard on ourselves; we demand too much, more than we expect of anybody else. We have keen memories and we keep a strict accounting.

I hung my head. After a moment I looked up and said, "To the extent that *my* long face conduces to the fog along this bar, I'll wash it off and beat my feet and sing."

for George

ADAM

"All these miseries prove man's greatness; they are the miseries of a great man, a deposed king."—
Pascal

1.

Longing to talk about love and awaken
in me longing again and bawl,
what sailor hot because of the sea
and death shall I recall, or which
of women to win and be her man?

For I was in a company of young people and they were talking about their loves, as they do, to cheer and excite themselves, some telling wistfully what they long for, some boasting about what they have, others lying. They became very
merry, one man talking about a whore, a woman about a
sailor. One father sweetly mentioned his children, and another man said that he was in love with a dog. I too wanted

to talk that way and be cheered and I blurted out, "The one I love is red—" and I burst into tears and began to bawl. For whom I love is Adam. He is the only thing I am in love with in this whole world, and I cannot find him. I could not continue speaking.

For nearly fifty years, I have been tirelessly seeking in the city and the country and in Europe. I have grown tired and I am still seeking. Listening to those young people, I understood my life work. Therefore let me describe also this beloved of mine in a mixture of prose and verse, imitating how long ago Dante wrote about Beatrice in *The New Life*; but I am doing it in order to console, with this beautiful subject, my aging and frustrated life. In order, being a poet, to have something to praise that I love, as other poets do; better than being dumb.

> —What loyal animal that hardly
> understands love dumb like my penis?
> what child of mine exciting because likely
> or giant for his size is lovable?

> *None* of these provokes me. Only you
> Adam, my red lover made of earth,
> I am in love with in this world.
> I talk about you and awaken
> in me longing again and bawl.
> My hard eyes soften when I look at
> your likeness by Michelangelo
> and my soul is mad with your surprise,
> namer of the beasts.

My sailor hot with sea and death!
my farmer on the mountainside!
my woman to win and be your man!
my animal dumb like my penis!
my child whose other name is Likely!
my giant for your size is lovable.

So I make verses about him, because a poet has to have *some-thing* to praise. But the truth is that I don't know whether Adam exists or is a figure of the mythological past or is a figment of my mind. I walk the streets, and even the fields and woods where no one at all is to be found (as if, if I found some one there, it would be more likely to be Adam). Naturally people gossip about this inept behavior of mine, but I don't care about that; though when I think of my wasted life, I burst into tears. It is stupid what I do; but it has kept me naive and my will for mankind alive. Man-like my god I make—

> Man-like my god I make nor fear
> to be an idol's fool, for
>   so hard I think of man the thought
>   crumbles into absolute
> un-Nature. Oh and he will save
> me in the little work and love
>   I lust in day by day until
>   my name he elects to call.

What I do know, however, is that my friends, such as regard me, say that I am a sad man; and even I can judge that the books I write are sad.

2.

In common day, my Adam is surprised; for everything happens to him for the first time. With present eyes he says, "Lo, here you are."

Oh, no doubt that his eyes are present as the brooks flow into eternity (as Rilke said of the animals). Nevertheless, he is shaking his head from side to side and, being a man, doesn't know which way to turn. "Lo! lo!" he says and his forehead is perplexed, "here now you are for me and here am I responding as who can?"

But an explorer to whom each new turning opens out a broader wilderness is finally afraid that he is getting lost and may not find his way home. But Adam is going in the only world that there is, even though to his grief and confusion. *He* is not lost. He goes firmly.

He does not, as in a hostile company, turn to each blow *after* it has struck, but he is ready where it comes like a fist between his eyes. My Adam is not insulted by being amazed, as if it were the part of dignity to be in the know, for *he* does not make a comparison between himself and others, what it is appropriate for a man to be like.

Adam is not disappointed when he is confounded, for he has not had any expectations; and the tears that start readily into the eyes of my beloved do not come from hurt feelings. As firmly he continues on his way to work, I wish that I could walk beside him silently a mile. In common day.

> When Adam woke a boundless surprise
> was his, to see his own flesh red,

to see the as-yet-nameless zoo parade,
and red the sunset and the white moonrise.
He was astonished when before his eyes
sat Eve, and afterwards both shame and dread
were news to him, and with uplifted blade
Michael at the door of paradise.

Everything that Adam fell was new.
When like himself the setting sun he shone
red on the hill and there stood Cain his son
but Abel on the field whom Cain slew,
he was amazed that him the quiet one
did not acknowledge as he used to do.

With Adam firmly walking to
the farm-work that he knows to do
   in deep confusion, for the grim
   news of everyday to him
happens each thing by surprise
like a fist between the eyes
   —let me day to day work on
   in this thick cloud that has sunk down.

In the Sonnet I remind myself that Adam is amazed, and in
the Little Prayer I pray that I too shall be able to continue
working even in this confusion that I cannot shake off. In the
following poem I express the wish that I could share in his
surprise:

      Day! save me! I am entranced
      by the Eternal Forms;
      by love and loss are they strong,
      by love and then by loss.

By love they came to be
and by death they are.
O unpeople me, my Day
my only one, this place

of sorcery where I lie,
and let only surprise,
surprise and falling asleep,
surprise and sleep be my gait,

surprise as when forth cast
from the finger of God the Man
looked back at him with boundlessly
boundlessly open eyes.

3.

This image of the creation of Adam that haunts me is in
the picture of Michelangelo's on the ceiling of the Sistine
Chapel in Rome. Yes, it is that trust-drunken face and its
present eyes that I am looking for in the factories and in the
fields.

And I have had the thought to arrange Michelangelo's picture as a dramatic tableau for the stage. The stage is divided
into two, and stage right (the spectator's left) is at first con-
cealed with a scrim.

Slowly from Left Rear appears the great cart of God and
his Angels, moving in an arc toward the center. It is wrapped
and blown round by the fluttering cloak of Whirlwind who
spoke to Job, noisily agitated by a wind-machine. But the
machine quiets down when the Angels begin to speak.

What are the Angels saying, as their cart swings toward the center? For at the decisive moment at which Michelangelo chose to portray them, their countenances are expressing the most various thoughts, as if they had been thinking or speaking; and there is no doubt that thus the poetic painter meant to tell us *his* different thoughts about the creation of Adam. The fat boy, attentive over God's right shoulder, is wide-eyed, a bit alarmed. The three who are looking over his left shoulder are like three youthful scientists, one wonderstruck with mouth agape, one with his lips grimly intent, and the third, looking straight at it, excitedly curious, with the small smile that we wear for the crucial experiment. But the lovely youth (or is it Eve?) about whose shoulders God's left arm is familiarly flung, and who is clutching at God's forearm for support and almost as if to check him, surely his face is big-eyed with dismay. What does it mean? And lastly, the chubby child on the right, whom God is touching with a bent forefinger, he is purposely *not* looking on at the scene but seems to be in a kind of daydream. And besides these, there are faces hidden in the shadows.

As the cart of God and his Angels approaches the Center of the stage, God has stretched out his right arm and forefinger, and now as if by the sweep of his gesture the scrim is opened, disclosing Adam on the hillside with his extended hand. There is no doubt that at some instant their fingertips have touched, but already the cart is continuing in its slow arc toward the exit Left Front, although God, as he goes, does follow with his eyes his creature.

At the moment of touching, too quick to be noticed, God has thrown Adam into being, and this is expressed by opening the scrim revealing him on the hillside. But there is no need for the actor of Adam to imitate the countenance of that moment, nor did the painter paint it, nor can we guess it; for already it is past, and Michelangelo has painted us the countenance of Adam at the instant after their fingers have touched.

This is the trust-drunken face of Adam with boundlessly open eyes, for his soul is pouring through his eyes looking into God's face that has not yet vanished. (As it has not yet vanished.) The look of my Adam is more alive than the solemn look on an animal's face; but it is more melancholy than the simply serious look of a man absorbed in his concerns. Adam has on his face the trusting and boundlessly-drinking look of separation from God, as if to say, "Lo! here now you are for me—going away, and here I am responding as who can." Not a look of grief, for God cannot be altogether lost. Nor a look of disappointment, for Adam has not had any expectations. But it is the look toward God going away, separated from us, just as it is. And after the cart has made its exit, this look does not change, but it is what the spectators take home with them, as the curtain falls.

This is the face and the eyes of my Adam, in his portrait by Michelangelo, that is fixed in my soul, and I do not know what to do.—

> Creator of the worlds! O joy
> of speed! and when the powers that lie
> latent, into being break,
> I shall not fear the onward wreck
> because I am in love with
> the nature of things unto death,

and as they loom say, "Lo!"
Lord favor me, the road I go.

Father! guide and lead me stray
for I stumble forward straight my way
    undeviating, I do not
    notice the pleasant bypaths that
make us this world surprising nor
the precipice that sinks before.
    O give me ground for next a step
    to stagger walking in my sleep.

As I think of my Adam thrown into this world whose resources I have assayed for fifty years of my life, to God I pray
for faith, for the conviction that I have ground underfoot for
a next step.

4.

So into this paradise that is a world for him, though often
to his grief and confusion, my Adam has awaked-like-the-slow-
avalanche-softly-snapping-trees. In common day when-after-
the-hurricane-everything-is-dirty-and-washed. Whichever way
a man looks-he-is-confronted-by-the-oval-wall-of-closely-fitted-
adjacent-colors. He cannot find a door in the day to go
through and come outdoors. Yet in-whichever-direction-a-man-
moves-he-brings-into-being-a-new-space.

Or if, sitting on his hillside, he is scrutinizing a stone that
he has picked-up-for-it-is-to-hand, suddenly empty freedom
has departed from him; he is pinned-in-the-attention-that-he-

chooses. But when he flings away the stone, the scenery has bounding-leaped-toward-him-up-the-hill and joins onto his unbroken space quietly-as-a-great-jumper-comes-down-and-ju st-walks-away. And into this unbroken space he steps.

Now Adam and the Sun are staring-at-one-another-each-waiting-for-the-other-to-volunteer-to-do-what-both-wish-but-ar e-not-able-to-begin. And Adam's sun is bigger than mine, occupying nearly one eighth of his sky. It is because he does not have so many other ideas in his field of vision, to crowd out the sun. The sun's hot rays come to him quicker than the eight seconds that they take to traverse to me.

Therefore Adam has made a plain gold disk about five inches in diameter. It is only metal hammered thin, but being a disk and being of gold it is an adequate image of the sun. One can gaze on it a long time as if warmed by its rays. I have seen many such sun-disks in the museums, coming from Central America or Ireland. I seek them out because my soul is cold, and I gaze at each one a long time and am warmed by its rays.

As a man of letters I have thought a lot about how Adam speaks, and I am persuaded, with Otto Jespersen, that his language consists of complex words, "inseparable irregular conglomerations that he is forever crooning." And Adam means his language to be a magical act in the world and change the situation, you, the thing, himself; otherwise he is left, like me, with an empty poem. So we may (imitating his own speech) describe him naming the animals in paradise: His-sensitive-surfaces-have-become-moist-and-he-is-reaching st anding-at-the-edge-not-quite-willing-to-dive waiting-out-the-int erval-between-the-flash-of-lightning-and-the-crash-of-thunder h

e-comes-down-softly-like-a-great-jumper-who-just walks-away a
nd copiously-as-the-warm-semen-spurts he calls out Tiger-tiger-
burning-bright-in-the-forests-of-the-night   thank-you-it-is-now-
my-grateful-privilege-to-oblige-*you*-how?

But alas! the tiger, who has small speech nor need for
friends, crashes-away-through-the-brush, leaving Adam with
the Name that he has acted.

Adam and the Name are staring-at-one-another-each-wait
ing-for-the-other-to-volunteer-to-do-what-both-wish-but-are-not
-able-to-begin, and Adam flaming with shame from his toes to
the roots of his hair, having dared to create something in
blinding forgetfulness of who he is, wanting-to-drop-out-of-
sight. But he is consoled by the approving embrace of the
Creator Spirit who hovers in the garden made for Adam,
though often to his grief and confusion. Let me pray.

> Creator Spirit, who dost lightly hover
> whence I know not and why to me I never
>   questioned, come. Do visit thy lover
>   after thy long absence. I turn over
> awaking in the morning, thou art not
> there to my touch, nor is a substitute
>   there, but nothing nothing at all to talk
>   to and make love when I awake.
>
> O Spirit wise, shine, somewhere shine
> so I can squander me again!
>   I ask it if ever I tried hard
>   to eke me out a livelihood
> from a grudging city, or if ever
> I have been patient to preserve

Opportunity my sweet
muse, my darling, my flirt.

And Adam is alert-to-the-noise-of-a-snake-in-the-grass. But
it is the snake himself, and Adam softly follows his swift
curviline arrow-straight to where, as D. H. Lawrence once
saw him, he is sipping at the water trough. Delighted with
the beauty of his guest, yet Adam holds-back-with-patient-
courtesy-in-order-not-to-disturb-somebody-eating. At length,
however, the snake looks up at him with his hard bright eyes.
There is an eerie-of-unresponsive-eyes, of looks-holding-one-
another-at-more-than-arm's-length. Adam is-frigid-at-the-prese
nce-of-a-spirit-whom-he-does-not-want-warmly-to-embrace; yet
he is-profoundly-respectful-of-the-equal-king-of-another-realm,
he himself being a fearless lord and king. The snake not-
swiftly-and-not-slowly slithers into a black crevice in the rock
and vanishes into the burning bowels of the earth, leaving
Adam with-an-empty-thought. Adam and the Black Hole
stare-at-one-another-each-waiting-for-the-other-to-volunteer-to-
do-what-both-wish-but-are-not-able-to-begin. While the proph-
et-birds in the branches are wildly hopping about, peeping
and grieving.

A dog is watching there, wagging his tail uncertainly, not
knowing if he is going to be regarded, more than ready to
make friends and be the dog of his master. Finally Adam
cannot not notice his dark limited gaze following his every
move as though it were a great matter.

So Adam stretches out, noblesse oblige, his great hand and
lays it on the dog's head, with the-slight-abstractedness-with-
which-one-gives-a-sufficient-satisfaction-to-the-other-when-it-is-

no-great-matter-to-oneself. He is pierced by the woeful pang
of being a superior being and alone. But the dog leaps up on
him in ecstasy, frantically wagging his plume, and barking
ear-splitting volleys echoing in the valley, until the man is
flustered.

5.

But *those* were, you say, the deeds of Adam in paradise,
whereas the Adam whom I love is no longer in paradise, if he
ever was. I tell you flatly, my Adam is as much in paradise
as he ever was.

To my mind the most dismaying moment in John Milton's
story about Adam, and one of the most awful moments in all
literature, is when, in the Tenth Book, God bids his Angels to
derange the world as "sorted best with present things." Then
some of the Angels laboriously push askant the axis of the
earth twenty degrees and more, entailing the consequences
of that; and others sow discord among the beasts. And the
world becomes just as it is. The world becomes just as it is.
It is hard work to accomplish it, Milton says so, but he does
not show us, like Michelangelo, the expressions on the faces
of the Angels doing that work. Naturally to me as an artisan,
with our obsession to conserve the least object of creation,
this command of God is the most sickening and shocking
possible, to derange what has been created good. I freeze with
horror when I read of those great Angels with their great
crowbars; and when I think how what Milton says is also
true, I burst into tears of woe.

And it is then that I think, with tears of joy and longing, that my Adam is practical, and he is *firmly* going to his farmwork that he knows to do, even though in deep confusion and surprised and balked.

I do not like it when people speak of Adam's "fall"; there is no such language in the Bible. How did he fall? from what dignity? how humiliated before whom? I agree with Pascal that his misery proves his greatness, for only a great man has such misery; but he is not a "deposed king," he is always a king, only his kingdom is in permanent insurrection. It is possible to construe the Biblical sentences about knowing and nakedness to mean that Adam has lost his innocence; but to me at least, this does not seem to be our universal fact. For although many people are knowing, ashamed of their nakedness, or otherwise no longer innocent, many of us are innocent and ignorant, surprised and confused.

But that the world is no longer very practicable for us, if it ever was, *this* is our universal fact. It does not offer us opportunities for our best capacities; it is rare among men that an occasion occurs at the right time (so that, when it does, we regard it as a gala day in history). And neither I nor the people I consort with are practical to seize even such opportunities as there are. But my Adam, whom alone I am in love with in this world, is practical. And if one day I have gold to give him, he will not demand but silver. Or nothing. Or be suspicious of counterfeit.

By "paradise" I mean nothing but the world practical. It is a matter of degree. Some people at some times have a more practicable world than others, and we say that they have

Grace or Luck. The world is a world for them. Naturally they have abounding faith, the conviction that there is ground underfoot for a next step. Others, by character or destiny (it comes to the same thing), have less luck; and I am one of those. I am in the middle rank, for I have been able to work, and therefore it must be that an area of the wide world is for me, in which I work. Goethe said, A man must do not what he wants but what he can—though he, to be sure, commanded a commodious area that was for him. Others, again, seem to have no luck at all. The world is not for them. And when I notice this, I do try to help and be some luck for them, in order that my world shall be more like paradise. (But with the best will in the world, it is hard to be somebody else's luck. The trouble is that I do not simply love them, thoughtless of paradise, for it is only Adam that I love.)

> Despairing to be happy any more,
> on the other hand I am not much in pain,
> I can work, and sometimes from my pen
> such lovely sentences of English pour
> as I am proud of for their casual grandeur
> nor will, when I am dead, they be forgotten:
> I look about and I am as most men
> as happy. Yet my spirit is still sore
> with disappointment of the paradise
> lost that I could not enter; a hard question
> haunts me, "Is life worth it as it is?"
> like a baffled man looking for the direction
> from side to side I shake my head—and oh
> notice! my toes are tense, to go, to go.

217

On the highroad to death
trudging, not eager to get
to that city, yet the way is
still too long for my patience,
teach me a travel-song,
Master, to march along
as we boys used to shout
when I was a young scout.

In the Sonnet I wonder whether or not I can indeed continue in the unhappy way I am in, and in the Little Prayer I pray to God to teach me a travel-song.

6.

Guard me from hope. Give me days of labor and a few moments of joy, but spare me the poisonous hours of hope in which I have lost touch with my only world, such as she is. Let the moments of joy be scattered, so I may not forget that that exists; but guard me from my feverish expectations that have never yet, and will not, come across in my real world. Wishes are chaos and—I don't know how it is with others— the color of my chaos is pain. I am not unobservant, and I know from experience the modest degree of success that comes to me, at what grade of paradise I live. Just enough to keep me going. Then, Lord, let me aspire according to my experienced judgment. (But if it be your plan, as you seem to have marked out, for me to exist periodically in the crazy distraction and torment of hope like a fever, I have been able to survive it till my forty-eighth year.)

Thou invigorating poison
that while I flush and pant
tossest me sleepless
Hope! only last night
in pain and joy I forethought
to wryly praise thee dread
drug I could not sleep,
and now tonight I neither
can sleep until at last
I'll cry myself to sleep
and let go of my life,
for thou hast not so much
vanished as grimly shone
thine other thy real face
Expected Disappointment.

O answering Luck! us who are agile souls,
who do the necessary and think up
new things—and sometimes we have adventured
into rough places among enemies,

then do you, O subtile O understanding
answering Luck! smile at and accompany
some of us, and they are laureate with
shining success and roseate with pleasure;

we others, though, look after wistfully
as you two vanish and the door closes;
it tastes us bitter and we would to God
we had been idle, we should be less hurt.

Tell me, Lord, is not my longing for his beauty the only
direct awareness that I *have* of paradise? How else can I know

it? It is the kind of knowledge that moves to action, and that unlooses also energy in me to squander.

But in my city, knowing about paradise I have become stupid. I am a mono-maniac. (Everything else is a lie.) The streets I walk are now my jail. And

My anger has become
a settled rage. I look calm
 but I no longer wish to touch
 any flesh with tender lust.
Lord, give me back my lust to touch
beautiful flesh, or else teach
 me some otherwise to make sense
 of my experience.

Now dare I anything! O Warden
of the Drunk and Careless, guard me!
 for the reins that stay my course
 and hinder me are loose.
When forth I go, for forth I shall,
my blond and black horses gallop
 toward the wreck that I forecast
 with little interest.

Such is the history of paradise that I have been able to tell in verses out of my life, better than being dumb.

7.

But Adam will make me take him seriously, and so stay my drunken and careless course.

It is hard for me to take other people seriously as existing, because I am smug and know it all, and I attribute to others needs out of my own ideas. (So finally I lose my attachment to my own life.) But Adam will not allow this to happen, he will not allow me to do it, and thereby he will give me a great surety in the world and an unaccustomed peace. Even if I am not going to be happy.

For we across these plains of hell are like the spinning dust-filled winds. My desires are fitful gusts, and I pay for them with airy efforts to serve people according to my pre-conceptions. My works vanish in eddies and whispers. Yet most of the people that whirl by seem to me even worse off than myself, whistling vortices of personality. And every-where, mounting high into the sky and blotting out the sun, are cyclones of dead leaves.

Adam is substantial. I cannot treat him, surprised and con-fused, as if he were an idea of mine. "I regret that I have not been of any good to you, Adam," I say. "I love you and I should be proud to see you happy and great, but I don't know how."

I don't say this to cajole a response from him, but simply because, when I am with some one I love, I cannot keep silent but compulsively need to express my affection in every word and act, and apologizing if I haven't been able to prove it. This behavior of mine is oppressive.

But Adam takes it simply as how I am. He does *not*, like the others, disregard my abject longing for him, as if I did not exist. (Because he acknowledges me, it will not so much matter if he loves me.)

"No, Everyman," he says, "you do me a lot of good. And

you *do* make me feel that you love me. I cannot disregard it. Everyman."

Oh! then I shall not have to talk bitterly about myself for my own ears as if I were a third person. *He* is substantial and *I* am substantial. The fitful winds calm down, and the strong sun of autumn is pouring upon us.

"You make a mistake, Everyman, to search for me so hard as you do. You could really sit quite still and I would know you by your work, how you love me. But it's a harmless mistake; I am not put off by it."

I will have lowered my eyes.—"Do you know my work? I am inscribing this present work to you, Adam."

There is a long pause. Yet I am *not* threatened by it, wondering what he is thinking. Adam can think his own thoughts.

"It has been peaceful, Adam, having you in my house this past week. Nowhere to go, having arrived. Also—" suddenly I am embarrassed—"your presence shines like a star."

(I *understand* that he does not love me; but this does *not* bring death to my heart, as I should have thought. Simply, that I in this world am not going to be blest and that—no newsy story—many a thing possible for others will not be possible for me.)

But to my stupefaction—as a man is understood and *therefore* the ground sinks from under his feet—Adam has said, "You have revived my purpose to succeed."

At this moment my hairs have stood up, electrified.

We are staring at one another each waiting for the other to volunteer to do what both wish but are not able to begin.

"Adam! let me pray!" and I shall pray the Little Prayer

God of the Fullness! who in hours
hast, after my starving years,
 filled my bowl and with garlands
 laden my outstretched hands,
teach me again what it is
to want, that I by long disuse
 and disappointment have forgot
 and my brain is slow with surfeit.

Naturally he is practical, and especially in this misfitting world where it is necessary to make an extra effort, he gives me and takes from me what satisfaction is possible, whatever the measure of it. And lo! suddenly! as a man is stung on the threshold by a wasp—I shall have been stunned by a sweet winged joy whose poison has now worked on me swiftly with such irresistible fire and power that I fell down as if I were dead. Among the howling and whining whirlwinds and the fitful gusts.—

I lustily bestrode my love
 until I fainted near and poured my seed
 and then I lay in sweetness like one dead
whom angels sing around him and above.

I lay with all my strength embraced
 and swiftly to a quiet grave withdrew
 most like a. grotto with the sea in view
surging and pounding, till the spell was past.

Since when my hours are empty of
 everything, only beauty touches me
 but is like pain to hear and see.
Absent among the tribes of men I move.

I am no longer careless of my life given to me and not made by me, as absent among the tribes of men I move.

8.

But I have had the thought that Adam is working all an afternoon tarring a roof in a clearing near Tenafly, across the river from New York City where I live. As he works and looks up he can often see, from the cliff-top, the slate expanse of the lordly river spreading northward, but not spangling, for the sun is sinking behind him.

Finally, having finished his day's work, he jumps down from the roof. And there, at the edge of the clearing, in a shaft of sunlight, stands the Angel Dogwood.

Adam is surprised. "Lo! here now you are for me," he says readily.

The resourceful Angel is one of those who come down from heaven and visit the world, wearing his white petals that are my bland joy. He is alive with empty spaces and shadows, and on him fall the shafts of sunlight as he stands here and there in the little wood, to make Adam smile. He is a resourceful and powerful Angel.

And Adam, tired with his day's work, gladly follows the Angel here and there in the wood and is surprised, espying the white dogwood in the sunlit woods. But when suddenly, as if to tease or excite him, the Angel puts on his pink petals, then Adam lowers his head stolidly and closes his eyes in pain, and turns to go home.

"Why, what's the matter, Adam?" asks the Angel pleasantly. "Why do you refuse in this way?"

And Adam says, "Your pink dogwood is too beautiful; it makes me yearn for the reunion of the separated and I hurt. But dogwood white is my bland joy. I look at you with an open face of wonder in the sunlit woods just on the border of the possible, and this doesn't make me unhappy."

So Adam was tarring a roof in the clearing of the possible and there stood, just on the border of the possible, the Angel Dogwood with his white petals, and Adam was not unhappy.

9.

And I have had the thought that it is sunset. Cain is standing in the field near the body of Abel whom he slew, when he notices his father Adam approaching on the road, returning from his work. Then Cain, his mind wandering a little, asks himself, "Lo! which of the creatures made by God in the Six Days is coming this way slowly? Is it the Sun downgoing in the evening, when he was new and did it the first time? Or the red Earth arising from the sea? He has the look of one who had no father—fearless! the first namer of the beasts: it is the Man, Abel's father." And as Adam draws near to where the murder is hovering near the ground, Cain has begun to shudder and be present in the world again.

Adam, acknowledging Cain, is surprised that Abel, the other brother, does not greet him, is not present. He calls out to the body Abel's name, but the body does not respond, and Adam is amazed. He does not choose to see the murder hovering near the ground.

"Lo!" he says, "lo! here now you are for me." For he knows

that Abel is dead like other animals, many of whom he himself slew. And he says to the Death of the first man to die, "Lo! lo! and here I am responding as who can." He too has begun to wander in his mind a little and to speak of himself in the 3rd person, and says to Cain, "Is Adam to be always learning? Everything that falls him is new."

But Cain says, "An Angel was here and we conversed. He put this sign on my forehead." He shows the mark on his forehead to his father, who examines it with wonder and curiosity.

"How comes Abel to lie still and not acknowledge me?"

"Because he is dead. I killed him with my hands, like a calf. He cannot move or talk or recognize *anything.*"

"Let me look again at that mark on your forehead, son," says Adam, and he examines it again with attention and curiosity. He keeps saying, "Lo! lo! here now you are for me."

It is a bad prospect, for he fore-knows that Eve is going to weep and mourn for the son whom she gave birth to with pain. The thought of it casts him into a gloom.

Seeing the trouble on his father's face, Cain feels excluded from his father's intimacy and is disturbed more than he can bear. (But in fact the murder that was hovering near the ground has gone away.)

Cain and Adam are staring at one another each waiting for the other to volunteer to do what both wish but are not able to begin.

But Adam helps him by asking a practical question. "What shall we do in this new case, I mean with the dead boy?"

And Cain says, "Let us carry the body back to my mother."

It is dusk, and where a man turns are holes in the oval

walls of closely fitted adjacent colors. There are loud holes like bells.

In the deepening dusk the holes are spreading, like loud bells. They are like loud holes, like bells. While Adam, carrying the body, says, "Lo! lo! here now you are for me—not. And here I am responding as who can?" For I have had the thought of Adam going confronting this only world that is for him, and he and she are staring at one another each waiting for the other to volunteer to do what both wish but are not able to begin. But Adam is practical and makes a gesture.

Such are some of the thoughts that I have had to praise Adam, whom alone I am in love with in this world, in order to console myself as I grow older.

> Thee God we praise, for this complete
> work that over-use and doubt
>   and pain could mar but not prevent
>   because thy spirit still was sent.
> Such as it is, this now belongs
> also among the created things
>   whilst I relapse, thy dying fact
>   more spent, more sullen, and more wracked.
>
> Heavy silence, Lord, dim eyes,
> dull ears, and dubious a guess,
>   I offer thee as that which is.
>   My tithe is this blind daze
> as I to work return
> without regard for past work done
>   and for the work I do begin
>   without reward or hope.   Amen.

NOAH'S VINEYARD

(after Michelangelo)

1.

After the Flood, everything was dirty and washed.
Noah began to be a farmer, and he planted a vineyard.
"How do you dare to do it, Noah?"
"Because," he said, "one day the prophet Isaiah shall arise
and prophesy: 'They shall build houses and inhabit them.
They shall plant vineyards and eat the fruit of them.'"
"When will *that* come to pass?"
"It will come to pass!" cried Noah. "It will come to pass,
saith the prophet, when God creates new heavens and a new
earth. Then a man will build and inhabit, and plant and eat
the fruit."
"But Noah! look about! is *this* new heavens and a new
earth?"

"No. Now I am just practicing."

The world was dirty with silt and new washed with water. The sun was hot and the plain was steaming. The farmer wore a straw hat, and bending his back to the spade he wore a little smile, as though he too had been promised something.

"What did He promise *you*, Noah?"

Noah leaned on his spade and said, "He promised me that while the earth lasts there will be seed-time and harvest, hot and cold, and night and day."

"He did not promise that you would plant and eat the fruit?"

"No, certainly He did not promise that. But that the seasons would henceforth be regular, and that *something* would come of it."

"Ah. Is this enough?"

He did not need to answer that, but fell to work. *Fell* to work, for in planting the vineyard Noah did not spade with his hands and wrists as if disdainfully; he did not work with merely his biceps and shoulders while holding his head away; but he bent his head and back to the spade, attending to what he was doing. And the power of gravity flowed up through his legs and back, and then around down into the spade into the clay. The spade shone lurid, and he remembered

2.

how the first flash of lightning had disclosed an instant face that seemed fixed at its widest scream. Simultaneously, as the successive lightnings flashed, that mouth had opened to its widest scream and so seemed stroboscopically fixed.

Because he remembered the Flood, Noah planted his vineyard in order to drink and get drunk. He was nagged by the long instant image of the scream, that lasted a frantic half hour. He was not much haunted by day when he was working the hot field, nor if, used up by his forthright labor, he ate and fell on his straw bed and slept. But if, being a man, he stood apart awhile, to look at the reviving earth, the spears of grass; and especially when he quit work early on the Sabbath eve. Then he was nagged, he nagged himself, with memories.

How the Ark is already afloat in the rain! This is occurring not all at once but for a frantic half hour, that the thousand-mile-long stormcloud has opened and the river runs over. Men and women have swum out to the Ark and are clinging to the plank; and the sons of Noah are swinging their oars to crush their fingers and get them off. One man is *unable* to let go in his despair, and one of the wives of the sons of Noah has lifted an axe. In the noise the screams cannot be heard, but in the lightning you can see an instant face fixed at its widest scream.

The intermittent lightning is blazing at every second, and simultaneously, the man sobbing and yelling is yelling *out* at every second: then his instant face out of the dark seems fixed at its widest scream for half an hour.

A man's memory is such a stroboscope.

When he is bending his back spading, Noah is entirely occupied in the rhythmic play of himself and the hot field. But if—like a man—he notices that the earth is reviving, and he himself is helping it to revive, he cannot but see that the spade is lurid.

Our father is planting his vineyard in order to drink and get drunk. Especially when, on the Sabbath, he raises high the stone goblet for all to behold and sings in his warbling and joyous bass, like the erotic bullfrog in the marsh:

"Sixth Day! and *finished* were heaven and earth and all their hosts. Blest art Thou, Lord our God and King of the Universe, who createst the fruit of the vine!"

Eagerly he drinks the cup and drains it.

3.

Now it is night. Noah is Pan, the leader of the bullfrogs in the marsh. It is night. Bigger beasts, the musk-ox and water-buffalo, have come down to listen, standing in the marsh, their belly-hair drenched. The hippopotamus is wallowing to his hips and shoulders. The frog is booming G-sharp in the bass. The moon is squirming in her sky-lake of light coffee, but in the mirror of the marsh the bright button of the moon is fixed and provocative: *you* must do it, O my lover, unbutton this tantalizing button and mobilize the breathing mud-depths.

Begoom, croaks our swollen father, on his great frond gently heaving—prophetic of later Moses in the bulrushes. The circles are spreading slowly to the fringed shore where only the nostrils of the hippopotamus are snuffling above water, yes and his gleaming eye in conjunction with the moon. The spreading concentric waves languish in the rushes; but tirelessly the patriarch thunders his *begoom* G-sharp in the bass, and the water-beasts are drunken with the song of Noah: he sings,

"Close your too bright eye, ferocious hippopotamus; do not look at us. So, let me unbutton—you! my world, my only one!—your garment too freshly laundered, it smells too fresh. Your garment, my only world! clasped by this bright button. My fingers are fumbling and you smile queenly at me. But I am persistent, no? Begooooom!"

The moon is pale and he is booming on a single note in

C-sharp minor while, for a swelling moment, the arpeggio soars and sinks.

It is still. Noah is unbuttoning the too freshly laundered garment of our only world in order to drown. His fumbling fingers have unbuttoned it. The splash that you hear is his diving from his black frond into the depths. He is squatting at his panic ease on the mud bottom. You cannot see him, but the bottom is exhaling bubbles of methane breaking at the surface. And the veil of the world is lying in a discarded and disregarded heap.

From his muddy home Noah the Pan is looking out with goggling eyes. Our world our only one has no clothes on. So passes a long time. The bottom is exhaling bubbles of methane that idly break at the surface. Our amphibious father is abiding a long time in the home of the drowned.

4.

Ham, that mocking son, whose name means Hot, looks in on him and sees his father's nakedness uncovered. For Noah is lying there sprawled in his drunkenness, leaking away as if it were tears.

"Whatcha doin' in there, daddy?" cries Ham, pretending to have a conversation with the drunken man.

"Who? me? Just pee-in."

"Well, for Chrissake, dad, you don' needa pump it out!"

Merrily Ham runs to tell the others, and they come to the door and exchange limericks.

But the frog's eyes are popping with attentiveness, awe-struck, as if he is seeing, we not. But indeed our only world has no clothes on, and you too might see her as well as Noah if you plunged into the black and sat there still, and breathed in softly the methane of the drowned.

"Mademoiselle!" sings out Ham,

> "Mademoiselle! let me persuade
> you to *a tergo* be laid,
>   so if, heaven forfend,
>   we are stuck in the end,
> out of here we can *walk* for first aid."

Shem more drily recites,

> "Prim, a poodle, trotting at random
> saw bicyclists riding a tandem.
>   With a horrified wail
>   she emptied a pail
> of hot water on 'em to disband 'em."

And Japheth, finally, favors them with the abstract theory of all limericks:

> "A character from a place
>   is doing what's a disgrace,
>   is hurried rapidly
>   to a catastrophe,
>   and in the dénouement loses face."

5. *The Scream and Dance of Noah Sober*

Awakening, Noah screamed,

"My desire's left the house! It is alive. Here is the discarded garment of my only world, too freshly laundered, yet such as it is! still warm from her body—" And he plunged his face and all his senses into that senseless landscape, squeezing the strong cloth, sniffing for a little odor. He was sick with longing for his only world.

Apprehensively he looked about, to see if he was observed. He was thinking, "Dare I put this dress on? the discarded garment of my only world, and feel my belly and my breast in hers?" But he did not care whether or not he was observed and he dared to slip into the garment, the senseless landscape. And so the patriarch danced, writhing and squirming, the Dance of Putting on the Senseless Garment of His Only World.

The dancer writhed and panted and the sweat broke out on his face. How close were they two now! He was standing up into the lap. So he danced Unable to Breathe Because of Waves of Trembling. He danced With Fumbling Fingers

Undoing the Button on the Garment of My Beloved. He urinated and the hot water stained the lap of the robe and ran down between his legs. He danced The Hero Who Has Put On a Poisoned Garment.

Noah planted a vineyard in order to drink and get drunk. (After the Flood everything was both dirty and new washed.) "It will come to pass!" cried Noah, "when God creates a *new* heavens and a *new* earth, *then* will a man build and inhabit, and plant and eat the fruit thereof!" And Noah unbuttoned the garment of our only world.

Afterwards Noah screamed: "My desire has left the house!" And he danced the dance of putting on the senseless garment of the only world.

6.

In the course of time the very silt and debris of the Flood themselves grew grass and flowers. And it was all one again. One could hardly guess what had occurred.

But we paleontologists dig savagely for the antediluvian. Bones. We dig savagely for antediluvian bones. As if we said, "Brothers! this is inadmissible, what we see about us. It is incomprehensible. Therefore let us dig."

"Yes. I am a psychologist and this patient dares to come into my office as he is! How else should he come there? But this is inadmissible. It is incomprehensible. I cannot tolerate it. Let us rather dig for the antediluvian."

So we dig savagely for bones. We dig.

"Brothers! as for me, I am living a life with my family and

friends in this city that is inadmissible. We cannot be persuaded, we *will* not be persuaded, that this makes sense. It is incomprehensible."

Therefore we paleontologists dig savagely for antediluvian bones. We dig up bones.

Darlings! look at one another; this is simply inadmissible. It is inadmissible. Therefore we dig for the antediluvian. We dig savagely for bones. We dig for the antediluvian, and what we dig for is bones. We dig *for* bones and we dig up bones.

THE GALLEY TO MYTILENE

(after Thucydides)

"Take me up, sailors, into your
great ship and I'll tell you a story
to bring you peace."

1.

In chains, but still trying to gesticulate with his chained
hands, as if he still had something to say, but he had nothing to say and could not utter a sound, the envoy from
Lesbos watched the preparations.

The galley was equipped. The oarsmen began to climb
in and take their places. To Mytilene was a voyage of a day
and a night, and they would arrive tomorrow morning, carrying the sentence of doom.

As the twelve men and their captain got in, the ship settled
low in the water.

The captain clambered back onto the pier and cried
angrily. "What kind of tub have you given us here?"

"The fastest ship in the Piraeus, and you know it," said the port inspector, checking it off.

"I count twelve men and food for twelve and me," said the captain bitterly, "and it's like a cargo of lead."

"The men's hearts are heavy, that weighs you down."

The captain aborted a gesture. He jumped in and she listed, and when she righted she had settled to the oarlocks. "This won't get us there in a week," said the bearded captain, whining like a child.

There was also no wind.

It was soon after sunrise, but the port of Athens already lay as if in black noon. The customs building and the warehouse were white blocks and their shadows swallowed men up like holes in space. There was no color anywhere.

There was movement. In the absence of atmosphere and reflection, the far-off of the Acropolis smashed forward like a fist that slowly from afar hits you suddenly between the eyes. The water spread to the edge and fell.

The Lesbian envoy, who had failed in the plea for clemency, had been brought to witness the departure. Chained, he was guarded by two stony boys. They would not let him onto the pier and he stood at the edge of the shore, in the water up to his knees. His face was haggard but he could no longer weep. He had no more language. They had crushed him in the Council by repeating monotonously their one sentence, "Teach others not to rebel."

As if he were speaking to men of affairs, to men of letters, he urged arguments of rational, imaginative, devious policy, but they said only, "Teach others not to rebel." Very soon he came to the wailing and gnashing his teeth and hugging their knees, but they repeated only, "Teach others not to rebel." The Athenians were stupid.

He could not weep because they did not offer him, even in his defeat, a consoling handshake.

To his hot dry eyes his lovely native town, with its porticoes and colonnades of rose and blue, was already flaming and razed. The women were shrieking in his ears. The men were dead. He did not feel for any of this, the shock of it was past. Indifferently he watched the last haze of smoke on the horizon.

They unwound the lines. The galley scraped the bottom and lurched. The captain angrily shouted.

2.

Once under weigh, out of sight of the ambassador, they rowed hard forward. The naked oarsmen sat in benches of two, and they rowed ten strokes to the minute. They rowed the *actual* minute (it was counted) and after it the minute after it.

The galley made slow progress.

The oarsmen for such an important mission were not slaves but free athletes, past their ephebic year of service, but it was wartime. Indeed, they were the best of the best, the strongest of the fairest. Yet they rowed away the actuality as if they were naked slaves and as if their captain were beating them in anger. They, who were used to go armed and merrily to even idiotic battles.

But we must distinguish between the actuality, the reality,

and the existing. (Try! you will never be able to distinguish them.) The hot sun lit the ship, the sea, the oars, the fists of the oarsmen: the actuality was how it *was*, this was the reality.

Ordinarily, however, we can imagine away, we have already somewhat imagined away, from the actuality how it is, and the reality is also this imagination. But *their* imagination was frozen to the actuality, and they rowed. They did not let themselves think of the one thought that prepossessed them, and no two on a bench spoke. They made slow progress.

The rapid rhythmic rowing itself was exhilarating. They began to sing a loud chantey.

"Don't you think that something is coming after us?" an oarsman asked his fellow.

They both looked back over their shoulders.

Naturally others looked back, to see what they were looking at. (There was nothing.) For a moment the count was broken and they stopped rowing. At once the ship came to a dead stop.

The men looked at one another with the whites in their eyes showing. For ordinarily a body floats on a little by momentum; it has inertia and therefore velocity. This is its reality. It is *springing* forward, it is *reaching* toward. But not their ship. They were adding stroke by stroke to a dead weight that did not come alive.

Their heavy hearts were now at sea. In a towering anger the captain brought out his bull-whip. But it was noon and they sneered at him and elected to eat.

The food was tasteless.

Their imagination was pinned to the actuality because of an idea in the actuality that they would not let themselves think. Yet this idea was no secret to anybody.

"It's a rough deal," said one of the oarsmen finally, meaning the sentence of doom that they were carrying to Mytilene; or perhaps meaning the actuality that *they* were carrying the sentence of doom.

"To what are you referring," said his fellow carefully, because he was thinking of the same idea.

"Do you know anybody there?"

"Don't you know somebody there?"

Another sailor asked his fellow without prelude, "Do you know anybody there?"

"Don't *you* know somebody there?"

"What are you referring to?" said another, because his mind was blank. "One! —one! —one! —one!"

They rowed hard forward, stepping up the beat to twelve, and they laid a minute of it on another minute on another on another. They worked up a certain speed, so far as one can do this without blessed velocity. But persistently it kept seeming to them that there was another ship, some other ship, *not* this ship, not *this* ship. Pursuing them. They kept looking back. They hastened forward because they were being pursued. On the wide sea was nothing. The sun lit what there was, the one heavy galley and the sweating oarsmen.

3.

At Mytilene on Lesbos, the Athenian garrison stayed to itself on the peninsula, neither fraternizing with nor harassing the populace, while they waited for the mandate from home. They expected no leniency, and perhaps they were even conniving for the Lesbians, thinking, "Let them vanish in the hills, if they can." But the Mytilenians were imprisoned by their own terror and made no effort.

No one felt this terror, the shock of it was past. It worked within and inhibited motion before it arose. Looking at them, constrained by no visible guards, one came to ask in surprise, "Why don't they act on impulse? why don't they run away?"

Instead, they were *confident* that the Athenians did not seriously intend totally to destroy them. They interpreted in this sense the withdrawal of the garrison. Yet by withdrawing, the garrison had become uncanny to them. What was up?

During these days, the Mytilenians, a people famous for pleasure and license, did not make love. If they had felt their terror and sweated and trembled, many would likely have rushed into license for a little comfort. But they were frozen.

Some went to the temple of Apollo Savior of Orpheus. The statue of the god was, as always, smiling, and they interpreted this as a good omen, during the very hours that the galley with the mandate of doom was looming across the water toward them.

Yet late in the afternoon, when the galley, we know, had come only *half* way and was making no rapid progress, there suddenly spread the rumor that the ship *had* arrived, and it had brought the expected sentence of doom. At once some of the men cut their throats, before they could feel their terror. The women felt their terror and shrieked. The fear

unfroze in the marrow of their bones and many rushed into
love for a little comfort.

"I told you so!" said a man to his partner.

She shrieked with delight.

A neighborhood was set afire, the black smoke hung in the
dusk. The soldiers of the garrison had to come to control the
flames and save the city, whose people they soon expected
to kill.

No ship was to be seen, but everywhere arose grief and
wailing. It was bitter to them to notice the ironical smile
of the god, and they cursed him and blasphemed.

4.

Heavy between the two worlds, the galley rowed hard—
pursued, rushing toward the goal, making no haste on a
horrible errand.

But when the dusk came over the water and the sun no
longer lit their hands and faces, it was no longer so easy to
identify as one the actuality and the reality.

The surrounding world was dark. The inner place was blue.
Their faces and fists were blue. The wooden oars were pale.
The men had put on their woolen cloaks.

Behind them, the sky was still white and they kept looking
back into it.

They had eaten the confused amalgam of the actuality and
the reality and now, in the cool evening, they began to be
sick. Suddenly a man would haul in his oar and lean over the
side and vomit. The ship drifted sideways. Ashamed, the

angry captain was racked with cramps. He let go the governor and, with the tears streaming from his eyes, he vomited up the actuality.

"I told you so!" said a sailor, referring to the idea that another ship was coming after them, "*there* she is! my shy one! my wood-dove!"—And indeed, against the fading whitening behind them, that was whitening itself into darkness, you could not see what there was or was not, in the sea's gray holes. "*See* how she skims and flies! my beauty! my new ship! my new ship approaching in the sunrise! Her name is *Dolphin*. Do you know anybody on her? *Don't* you know somebody on her! Hurry, fellows, let's get on—because she never comes when you wait! She never comes when you look back at her! My gull! my delight! One!—one!—one! dammit! This is the last time I ever go to sea."

He spoke a little beyond their vital belief, and they jeered him good-naturedly.

They stepped up the beat, because it was very cold. They tried again a chantey. And to any one a few hundred yards away (but there was no one) would have come the sound of music on the water, welling from that dark ship, wasting in the holes of the sea. The first stars began to come in.

They kept looking back at the progress of the other ship that was bearing down on them.

5.

It is night and the city of Mytilene is at rest. Its heart has bounded its pulse. The knocking bones in fright have loosed the electric currents of vegetation, and they are flowing. There is no sign of life—

"All that mighty heart is lying still."

But it is *still* beating! Therefore the sentence of the poet is sublime. For indeed the mighty heart of the sleeping city is not still but is quietly beating. Even as you perceive that it is still, you know that it is not still.

6.

At sea the existing is gently arriving into the next moment. The existing is blazing here like the Burning Bush of the Jews where, if you plunge your hand, you take it out your existing hand. The fire is colored the color of passing-thought-over-a-face. So the fists of the oarsmen are lit up, and their faces are lit up and arriving.

Around midnight the other ship, named *Dolphin*, overtakes them.

They are hailed.

Blazing in the existing, the *Dolphin* lies off a way; she rides high in the water; her sail is bellying in the wind of desire. The tired oarsmen look at her with aching hearts.

"What do you want?" calls our captain.

The answer comes at once, loud and clear: "The Athenians have relented. The order to destroy Mytilene is countermanded. We are carrying a more hopeful message."

"How do we identify you? Do we know anybody aboard you?"

And the reply comes clear and loud: "*Don't* you know somebody aboard us? don't *you* know somebody aboard us?"

Circling, the *Dolphin* draws closer to us and comes their cry: "It makes no difference what you choose to believe, for you are about to sink, and we are on our way. So come aboard!"

It is true. Stopped dead, overtaken, without even the forward impulsion of the actuality, our ship is sunken to the gunwale and is certainly foundering.

"Hurry, damn you!" cries *Dolphin*, "before you all drown." "Move closer!"

Will tack as close as she dares, the sail flapping angrily and the sheets whistling in the inhibition. The sail drops. "Come! jump!"

The moon rises at a bound and we'll see how it is! We jump into the suddenly spangling sea. Angry father our captain is standing there, to see us safe away. Then he too jumps and swims for it.

Dripping with the moment we joyfully clamber aboard the *Dolphin*, filling out her crew to twelve and one.

A moment later, the other galley will have sunken.

Safe on our new ship, we men are beginning to weep, to burst out crying, and soon we shall be sobbing and bawling, and it feels good.

It is because of relenting. Some one has relented. Something has been relented.

We see that our misery was not inevitable, there have been other possibilities. Our imagination is no longer pinned to the one actuality. But of course the actuality itself has now changed, and this is the reality. (Try! and I shall never be able to distinguish them.)

Having let go, we have nothing to hold on to. It is for ourselves that we are crying, because of everything that has been lost. We are sobbing in self-pity, but we are bawling absolutely, in darkness and blackness. In newness and darkness and the void. Keeping our eyes open or shutting them seems to make no difference.

We, the strongest of the fairest! bawling on our new ship, and we do not know another minute to add to this minute. Opening our eyes or shutting our eyes makes no difference.

I am not at ease on the strange ship. The *Dolphin* rides too light in the water; a man does not feel himself sitting *in* her with his weight. Looking about, we recognize one another. (Where are the others?)

A favoring gale. Put up the sail. Pick up speed. After a while, take up the oars and also row. Desire! desire!

But for the moment we are doing nothing. Looking, not at one another, with open eyes. We are guilty because we have forgotten the *other* mandate, whatever it was. "Don't look at me!" cries the captain, as a teacher flinches before a child's imploring eyes when the problem is too hard, "the answer isn't written on *my* face." Rubbish! he doesn't know the answer either.

"Isn't there anything to eat? We're empty. We vomited up the actuality back there. Surely they didn't send a ship after us with nothing."
Will feed on the oranges of arriving.

7.

As our new ship approaches in the sunrise—
coming around the promontory
The sunrise is washing all rose and blue the colonnades and porticoes of Mytilene.

Before a favoring gale, leaning hard on the oars, adding yards and bursts of time and speed to the momentum and the previous and the wake, we have skirted the cliff and are already bearing down on the beach. Shall we anchor off or risk it and plunge through the surf?

At first flash, the colors of the city seemed to be almost baby blue and pink, but there is a depth of darkness in them that the sight gropes into, trying to touch solid. Navy blue and blood red.

The townspeople have sighted us! They are pouring down to the shore. As for us, we are *un*afraid to act out the resolutions made by night!

They are wading into the water. Obviously they count on good news—but this they could already guess from the rapturous rhythm of our rowing, the *added* bursts of our gale-borne flight—yes, as the swan regularly yet with a *steady* augmentation, drawing on no failing source, leaves the water, and flies, dripping the moment from his feet.

The gulls are so thick about us that it is hard to see. But the people can see *us* in the cloud of gulls. They are crying out confused sounds. The gulls are screaming.

Twin Castor O! and twin of Castor! what a thing it is to arrive!

The people's hearts are pounding as only with those bursts of confident hope touched by the uncertainty of the final moment. Let us be careful, for it is just such persons who recognize their happiness and drop down dead.

Now *here* is the surf. We are going to risk it and plunge through the surf and beach her. Our ship, our *Dolphin*, was designed by experience, that makes bold choices. The curve of desire is built into her hull. He found out our mother in the heart of the tree.

We have touched.

They crowd around, silent. The wash of the breaker is wet on the glad faces of our sailors and they are so bright and beautiful that I am struck blind.

Carefully—not delaying, but avoiding producing an exaggerated impression—we say: "The mandate from the citizens of Athens is not unfavorable to you; you need not fear the worst."

Hermes, thank you. You have given me to deliver a message that relieves fear. I say to a man, "Thank Hermes."

"Ah! we need not fear?"

"You say," says another man carefully, "that we need not fear the worst."

"We knew that they would repent!"

"The other ship was a mistake!"

"I told you so! that the *Athenians* could not let the other order stand." He speaks of them proudly, as if they were not the tyrants of his people!

Some of the women were leaving the beach with tears trickling down their cheeks.

"Repent?" one of our sailors caught the word. "*Other* order? What other ship?"

"The order brought by the other ship. The first ship."

"*Was* there another ship?!" we cried in consternation. "What? did *they* get here?"

We ourselves had *seen* that other ship sink in the sea.

"*How* did they get here before us?"

"Oh, it was not so bad, not so very bad," they reassured us. "Please don't be upset. In the first panic, as if the order had to be carried out at once! and by our own hands! a few killed themselves. A few houses were set afire—hard to know by whom. But I said, Wait! And now, thank God, you have come . . . Please! don't disturb yourselves so. A handful. Not too bad. I assure you."

I looked at my fellow. "They are here. We'll meet them. It's inevitable, in a small place like this. All of a sudden—coming round a corner—" Already in anticipation, vividly imagining it, the guilt of it had me by the throat.

"Oh, he's as afraid of you as you are of him. Did you know anybody on her?"

"Didn't *you* know somebody on her?"

So (otherwise than the history tells it) the galley brought to Mytilene a message of clemency.

By this time the Athenians too had relented.

ACKNOWLEDGMENTS

Acknowledgments are made to the following publications in which some of the stories included in this volume first appeared, either as here printed or in an earlier form: *Discovery No. 6*, published by Pocket Books, Inc. ("Our Visit to Niagara"); *i.e. The Cambridge Review* ("Bathers at Westover Pond" and "The Complaint of Richard Savage"); *Evergreen Review* ("A Statue of Goldsmith"); *Possibilities*, George Wittenborn, Inc. ("The Emperor of China"); *Quarterly Review of Literature* ("The Death of Aesculapius"); *The Kenyon Review* ("A Visit to Chartres"); *The Black Mountain Review* ("Noah's Vineyard"); *Botteghe Oscure* ("The Galley to Mytilene").